Dace:
The Prince of the Stream

By Dr Mark Everard

First published on June 2011

© Text - Dr Mark Everard

© Photographs - Dr Mark Everard

© Design - Mpress (Media) Ltd

© Cover artwork - Mick Loates

© Illustrations – Dr Mark Everard except for the two photographs of USS submarines SSN-607 and SSN-247 in chapter 3.2 *Where do dace get their name*? and also the drawings and paintings in chapter 3.4 *The art of the dace* which are credited to the talented artists who created them in that chapter.

ISBN NUMBER 978-0-9567015-6-5

Unit Four, Ashton Gate, Harold Hill, Romford, RM3 8UF

Designed and published by m press (Media) LTD.

Contents

Dace: The Prince of the Stream

Dace, those dashing silver natives of our flowing waters, evoke in my mind a childhood playing in fresh streams. They gladden me still, for the simple pleasure of watching or catching them but also through the knowledge that conditions are right for them.

I was asked at the outset of writing this book exactly who in their right mind would be interested in writing a book about dace. I am not sure I can answer the question as posed, but I do know that the kind of person who might be tempted to write about the world of the dace is the kind of person who wrote about such un-sexy fish as roach and small fry. Someone, in other words, not intent merely upon selling a million copies of books about the 'biggie' species that dominate the angling market, particularly carp and barbel. Not that I've anything against those fish per se or those that angle for them. It is just that the slighter species of fish that are less well covered by the angling media typify for me all that is good about being by the water.

Someone that would write a book about dace would have to value the sharp flows of clean water and the pure gravels that let them breed and prosper. They will in all probability be seduced by the flash of a passing kingfisher, the play of sunlight on riffle, the mew of a soaring buzzard and the rustling of aspen leaves on a summer zephyr. They will love wilder rivers for their own sake.

More to the point, who on earth would spend good money on a book on dace? The answer to that is probably that they will be the same kind of unhinged individual as the author, not seduced by the tackle catalogue and the pursuit of bigness as if it had any intrinsic value. This would be the kind of person for whom pleasant reminiscences about a day by the water dwelt not upon the weight of fish alone but also on a fleeting sight of the hunting sparrowhawk, the buzz of insects beneath the broken shade of a willow bough, a rope of minnow spawning on stream-washed shingle, and the first summer emergence of the frothy flower head of the bank-side meadowsweet.

This is a relatively little book, reflecting both the slight nature of the fish itself and the narrower audience who might read it. It is dedicated to all who value the streamy places that support thriving populations of dace and the ecosystems that sustain them.

Dr Mark Everard
Great Somerford, March 2011

Dace: The Prince of the Stream

Dace: The Prince of the Stream

Part I. The ecology of the dace

The inner world of the dace

To understand dace, angling for them and their relationship with human society, you have to delve into the inner world of the fish. You have first to understand the biology of the fish: what makes them 'tick', how they interact with their environment, and something about the environmental conditions that suit them. From this, it is possible to understand dace a little more objectively, or at least from a little closer to their own perspective.

Part I of this book concerns itself with the ecology of the dace, providing the reader with a bedrock of understanding that will best inform *Part II: Dace angling and Part III: Dace and society*. This echoes the structure and approach of *The Complete Book of the Roach,* in which I went into very great detail about all aspects of that species. However, it would not be appropriate to write such a heavy volume about so slight a fish as the dace! So, if you want more details, I suggest that you delve into my book on roach as many general principles apply equally to these two species.

The study of dace biology could form the basis for a very long book. However, for our purpose, *Part I* is restricted to those aspects that either bear directly upon angling and fishery management or are of general interest. If you are not of a scientific persuasion, don't fret! I have made the information accessible and in plain English, including Latin names where they are of interest but without expecting you read them if they are not. About this, I will simply echo the sentiment of Henry Sullivan Thomas, in his classic 1873 book *The Rod in India,*

> *"Do not be afraid of the natural history. There is not more of it than a good fishermen ought to know, and as it is expressed simply I trust it is not very uninteresting."*

Whatever your level of interest – and since you have picked up a book about the frequently-neglected dace then I assume you are already quite interested – I hope that you enjoy this book, and will learn a little too as I have done in writing it.

What is a dace?

A sensible starting place for this book is to ask what dace actually are. We'll delve briefly into the scientific discipline of taxonomy to help us answer that disarmingly simple question.

Dace taxonomy

Dace are fish (superclass *Pisces*), and bony fish (class *Osteichthyes*) at that. The bony fish comprise the overwhelming majority of fishes alive today, and occur in a wide array of shapes, sizes and life habits. Within the bony fishes, dace are found amongst the teleosts, which are the ray-finned fishes (superorder *Teleostei*). The teleosts include most living fish, comprising about 20,000 species worldwide which represent almost half of the vertebrate animals known on Planet Earth. They owe this dramatic success to four key features – a symmetrical tail, rayed fins, light and flexible scales, and specialised mouthparts – which collectively help them adapt to a bewildering diversity of habitats, diets and life histories.

Containing some 1,700 living species, one of the largest families of teleost fish is the minnow or carp family (family *Cyprinidae*), also known as the cyprinids. The cyprinids inhabit temperate and tropical fresh waters from Eurasia, Japan, most of the East Indian islands, Africa and North America. However, some members of the carp family have been introduced into many more waters beyond this natural range. The cyprinids have protrusive jaws, and lack teeth in the mouth but possess specialised throat teeth (pharyngeal teeth) which enable them to exploit a broad array of food.

The dace-like carps (sub-family *Leuciscineae*), one of a large number of sub-families of the carp family, are characterised primarily by the lack of barbules around the mouth. They occur mainly in Eurasia (excluding Arabia, India and South-East Asia), Japan, and North America.

Whilst the *Leuciscineae* have a long pedigree, giving rise to many species which thrive today across all manner of European waters, we know surprisingly little about the evolutionary pathway of the dace itself.

Dace present

Only one species of dace is native to the British Isles. This fish is known to scientists by its Latin name *Leuciscus leuciscus* (Linnaeus, 1758) and also known to anglers and naturalists as the 'dart' or 'dare' (for reasons discussed in Part III of this book). Dace are readily identified from a few characteristic features.

The dace is a slim fish, elongate and streamlined as befits a fish adapted to moderate to fast currents. Dace are fish of moving waters, preferring cool, running water though they may sometimes be found in lakes and in brackish water near the mouths of rivers.

Dace have a classic silver-sided counter-shading, which offers the fish a degree of invisibility to would-be predators by reflecting their surroundings. Viewed from below, the white or cream underside merges with the bright sky. Observed from above, the darker green to bronze back (depending upon habitat) merges with the stream's bed. Seen from the side, this graduation of colour over bright, silver and quite conspicuous scales reflects back the surroundings of the fish.

The fins are translucent, sometimes grey, often yellow-tinged and occasionally also suffused with a delicate pink (but never the strong red of a roach). This is not, however, universal and in many specimens, particularly smaller specimens and those from turbid waters, the fins are almost colourless. The head is slender, its precise shape considered by authorities as indicative of sub-species in continental Europe. The mouth is small and inferior (slightly under-slung) indicating a capacity to feed freely on the bottom but also to be adaptable to feed at all depths. The angle of the jaw does not extend back as far as the eye. Dace feed on flying insects of all kinds, the aquatic larvae of insects, worms, small snails, and also parts of plants including some filamentous algae.

Dace are not big or bulky fish, rarely exceeding 26 centimetres (a little over 10 inches) in length and 200 grammes (about 7 ounces) in weight, and with a maximum age of 10-11 years. However, there exist a few records of dace of over 30 centimetres (almost 12 inches) in length. They are also bony fish and, for this reason as well as their generally small size, they are not commonly eaten by humans. The Siberian subspecies, however, has some importance as a food-fish, and is caught with fixed gear, seines or on hooks. It is as a sporting fish that the dace incites the greatest human interest.

Dace of yesteryear

If you read angling or fishy literature from prior to the end of the nineteenth century, you may come across two interesting species that are unfamiliar today. These are the graining and the dobule.

In his classic 1879 book *British Fresh-Water Fishes*, the Reverend W Houghton listed and described the graining, with an illustration (reproduced below) by A.F. Lydon.

A graining.

The graining (*Leuciscus lancastriensis*) was said to look like a brownish-tinged dace, and in all probability was! It was believed to be confined to the waters of Lancashire. In *The Diary of A. J. Lane: With a Description of those Fishes to be Found in British Fresh Waters* (published 1843) the graining is described thus,

"In form somewhat like a Dace, but much rounder in the belly, tail deeply forked, top of the head and back a sort of drab coming down the sides and terminating rather suddenly; beneath this and the belly much lighter, eyes whitish, cheeks white, or yellowish, scales much smaller than in the Dace."

The British ichthyologist C. Tate Regan finally disproved the separate identify of the graining in his definitive 1911 work *The Freshwater Fishes of the British Isles,* explaining that, although the zoologist William Yarrell (1784-1856) was correct in his diagnosis of the fish's physical characteristics, they applied solely to the single specimen that he had examined from a small tributary of the Mersey near Formby. The graining then was merely a brownish-tinged dace from Lancashire!

The dobule, or dobule roach, is another dace-like fish of historic interest. Dobule (*Cyprinus dobula* Linnaeus, 1758 also later reclassified as *Leuciscus dobula* (Linnaeus, 1758)), were once thought to exist elsewhere across Europe. Again the dobule was first classified as a British species by William Yarrell, based upon a single specimen caught from the Thames estuary. However, there was doubt about the identity of the fish in the Reverend W Houghton's time as he writes in *British Fresh-Water Fishes* that,

> *"The Dobule Roach, a single specimen of which Yarrell took with the mouth of a White-bait net in the Thames below Woolwich, and which is regarded by Günther as a small Dace, is thus in its principal characteristics described by Yarrell..."*

The dobule, it turns out, was also just another dace out of place!

Lydon's painting of the dobule, from the Reverend W Houghton's British Fresh-Water Fishes.

Confusion with other species

Dace are a distinct species from other cyprinids and are not easily confused with many other members of that large family of temperate and tropical freshwater fishes. Tench, carp, barbel and other more robust cyprinid species of the British Isles are quite different in appearance. However, as dace lend their generic name to the 'leuciscine' (or dace-like) fishes then we should not be surprised at similarities and the potential for confusion with some other species in that sub-family. Other species with which dace can on occasion be confused include primarily chub, but also roach and bleak. We will explore below some of the similarities and differences.

C. Tate Regan, in his standard work *British Fresh-water Fishes,* states that,

> *"The Dace is closely related to the Chub...."*

This is a conclusion with which many other writers, both scientific and piscatorial including a fair few inexperienced anglers, have found themselves agreeing. This is true not only for small specimens, but particularly so for big dace which often have more of the 'muscular' appearance of a small chub than their lithe, delicate-mouthed smaller brethren. Fred J. Taylor is quoted once as noting that we *"...can spend our lives trying to catch a pounder and when we do it will be a little chub!"* John Bailey and Roger Miller, in their 1990 book Chub and Dace, admit that, even for serious anglers like themselves,

> *"...it can be possible sometimes to confuse a very large dace with a very small chub! It has certainly happened to us in the past with those occasional super 'double figure' dace — that is, a fish of over 10oz in weight."*

Once you get your 'eye in', it is hard to mistake the chub and the dace, but many people do including, by their own admission, some well-known anglers as well as other sources of seeming authority. As one example that E. Marshall-Hardy refers to both in his 1942 book *Coarse Fish* and the various editions of his *Angling Ways,*

"Writing in the London Evening News many years ago, I said: 'The largest dace of which I know was taken by Mr. L. Cookson from the Ivel (Beds) and weighed 1 lb. 8 oz. This specimen is to be seen in the Letchworth Museum. I think, however, there is some doubt about this fish, and believe it to be a small chub'. In response to this statement came the following letter… '…A re-examination of this fish by the authorities at South Kensington has revealed that it is a chub, and not a dace. It was presented to the Letchworth Museum as a dace and had not previously been questioned'."

Best then to check, and to know exactly what you are looking for, particularly where big dace are concerned. Fortunately, there are a number of distinguishing features differentiating dace from its more robust cousin the chub, *Leuciscus cephalus* (L.), without having to resort to counting fin spines and rays (discussed later in this chapter) or else killing the fish to dissect out its pharyngeal teeth for a more certain identification (not addressed in this book).

Many scientific and angling authors have highlighted these obvious morphological points. They are summed up succinctly in *Mr Crabtree Goes Fishing* by the late Bernard Venables as follows,

"The dace is rather like a small and more graceful chub. Novices, in fact, often confuse the two species. But this confusion is quite unnecessary. There is one thing alone which can remove all doubt. This is the shape of the anal fin. In the chub it has a convex edge. In the dace it is concave. Besides this, in the chub it is red, and in the dace it is not. The dace may be expected in shallow water of brisk flow."

The most obvious and reliable distinguishing feature is indeed this distinction in the profile of the anal fin. That of the dace is concave (curved inwards), whilst that of the chub is convex (curved outward).

The second key distinguishing feature to look out for is the mouth. That of the dace is generally more delicate and more easily protruded, whereas a chub's mouth is huge and generally white-lipped. The build of the chub, the head in particular, is far sturdier than that of a dace. Chub also have far more squared tails and, unlike the slighter lips of the dace, the mouth of the chub extends back to under the eye.

Other authors emphasise the colour of the fins. In the 1958 book *Dace: How to Catch Them,* William J. Howes notes that,

> *"The ventral, pectoral, and anal fins are yellowish, sometimes with a slight tinge of very pale pink. This is not always the rule, however, as many specimens have been caught with these fins almost colourless; a watery colour in fact. The tail (or caudal) fin is forked. The head is comparatively small, with a conspicuously brilliant eye."*

Within this description of fin colour, Howes also highlights the flaw of relying too heavily upon colour. Fish of all species are incredibly variable in colour as a result of genetic factors but perhaps more so in their adaptation to the conditions in which they are found. Stillwater dace and those from murky waters in particular can look very 'washed-out', and elsewhere the pink highlights may suggest a certain 'roachiness'. The shape of the fins and head and the position of the mouth are better physical indicators.

Small- to medium-sized dace can sometimes be confused with roach of similar size, particularly where both fish coexist in streamy rivers and where the roach may be leaner in appearance than specimens from still or slow-flowing waters. It is generally noted that the eyes of dace are yellowish, never red like that of a roach, and that the iris has a small, dark spot. Furthermore, roach are generally plumper with red fins. Whilst colour is a notoriously unreliable feature from which to make a definitive identification, I do not disagree with this general appraisal. Again, for a definitive identification, count the number of fin spines and rays as well as that of the scales along the lateral line as noted later in this chapter.

For some people, there is difficulty in determining dace from bleak. It was once assumed that dace did indeed cross-breed with bleak, but the eminent fish biologist Tate Regan determined early in the twentieth century that the scarce fish once identified as bleak x dace hybrids were in fact bleak x chub hybrids. This author knows of no authenticated reports of dace hybridisation with bleak. Smaller specimens of dace can appear superficially like bleak, but the tell-tale signs, aside from the generally more blue-green coloration over a more pearly flank of the bleak, is that a bleak's mouth is angled markedly upwards and, the definitive feature, the anal fin is very much longer albeit still with a concave outer edge.

Images of (from top to bottom) dace, chub, roach and bleak on the same scale to help you look closely at the key morphological differences described for the species.

The overall impression of a fish as an angler swings it to hand (i.e. the general feeling for a plant or animal known in wildlife-watching circles as the 'gis', short for 'Gestalt') that I have found to be the most reliable upon subsequent more detailed exploration of features are that:

- Roach have a general 'redness', and the red eye is often quite striking;

- Chub are generally more chunky with a big mouth, and the red ventral and anal fins contrast markedly with the black or dark dorsal and tail fins; whereas

- Dace are slighter and silvery with a pronounced downturn of the mouth.

To make a definitive identification, scientists rely upon counts of the spines and rays of certain of the fins, and on the number of scales along the lateral line (as well as above and below it on occasions). These are documented in a comparative table of those fish with which dace can get confused.

Leuciscine Species	Rays in Anal Fin	Rays in Dorsal Fin	Scales along lateral line
Dace	III/8	III/7	48-51
Chub	III/7-9	III/8-9	44-46
Roach	III/9-11	III/9-11	42-45
Bleak	III/16-20	III/8-9	48-55
Ide or Orfe	III/9-10	III/8	56-61

You will have noticed that I have included the ide or orfe (*Leuciscus idus*) in the table above. The ide is not native to the British Isles, being naturally distributed across eastern Europe and through into northern Asia. However, 'golden orfe' and 'blue orfe' coloured strains are widely available here as ornamental fish, and can turn up, the 'golden' variety in particular, in our rivers. (Indeed, as I write, I hold the Bristol Avon river record for the golden orfe for a fish of 2lb 6oz 4dr taken in March 2003.) However, there are a number of British rivers, Surrey's River Mole to name but one, where ide have naturalised, reverting to their natural silvery colour and looking decidedly dace-like.

These fish prefer still or slow-moving waters. How easy is a naturalised ide to confuse with a dace? Quite easy to the unfamiliar eye, though the snout is blunter (like that of a chub), the mouth is distinctly oblique unlike the small, slightly under-slung mouth of the dace, the dorsal fin is convex (outward-curved) and the anal fin is longer-based with a convex or straight edge. A distinctive feature is the less obvious scale pattern of the ide, due to a covering of more and smaller scales reflected in the significantly higher scale count along the lateral line.

Hybrids

Cross-breeding, or hybridisation, occurs widely between closely-related fish species. This is particularly so where human-induced changes mean that the barriers between species are broken down during the breeding period. For example, hybrid coarse fish species are substantially more common when rivers or lakes are over-managed and in artificial water bodies, where a paucity of spawning substrates leads to competition for spawning sites and a consequent co-mingling of spawning adult fish.

Also, where fish not native to a particular water become introduced, hybridisation with stocks of native species are more frequent. Classic examples include the free hybridisation between the native crucian carp (*Carassius carassius* L.) and the introduced but now widespread goldfish (*Carassius auratus* L.), which now threatens to exterminate the crucian carp as a pure species in the British Isles.

Various species of leuciscine fishes – the dace-like fishes of the sub-family Leuciscineae which includes roach, chub, bream, rudd, bleak, silver bream and dace – interbreed freely. For example, roach cross quite commonly with common (bronze) bream (*Abramis brama*), rudd (*Scardinius erythrophthalmus*), and silver bream (*Blicca bjoerkna*) in British waters, and hybrids with bleak (*Alburnus alburnus*) and chub (*Leuciscus cephalus*), whilst not common, are not unknown.

The exception to this relatively free flow of genes between leuciscine species is, however, the dace, with which hybrids are not known. Well, not known in the UK at least; there are sporadic though not necessarily completely reliable records of dace x ide hybrids in continental Europe. The principal reason for this is probably the timing of spawning, which is a topic we will return to later in this book.

In closing this discussion of hybridisation and the dace, it is worth a quick mention of the views of E. Marshall-Hardy. In his 1942 book *Coarse Fish*, he asks what he refers to as an impertinent question about the parentage of dace themselves. Referring to a 'certain strictly preserved' trout fishery which had also been stocked with roach and chub, Marshall-Hardy notes that, *"All went well for a while, then the Trout, Chub and Roach diminished in number and the water was heavy with Dace. From where had they come?"* Marshall goes on to ask the reader,

> *"...how often does one find Chub and Roach in a water without Dace? ...Could the Roach and Chub be responsible for the Dace? ...Be my question the result of a mere flight of fancy or at best a fantastic speculation, it has served to produce what is tantamount to a denial of such possibility from my friend whose scientific attainments and dicta merit the reader's respect. However, the facts foregoing are, I think, worthy of retention if only as matters of interest."*

Marshall-Hardy goes on to seek the reader's excuse for *"...the streak of devilry which prompted the writer's question"*. Fortunately, detailed physical records, reproductive studies and modern genetic analysis assure us that dace are dace and not a product of the co-mingling of other species!

Other European dace

Whilst there are no other species of dace in the United Kingdom, *Leuciscus leuciscus* is not the only species of dace in Europe. In fact, several other species of dace are found across the rest of Europe, although there is some scientific debate about whether these are or are not merely different forms of one species. Of all these 'dace', *Leuciscus leuciscus* is the most widely distributed. The other European relatives of the dace have been described from Dalmatian and Croatian rivers and lakes. Relatively little is known about them and they are difficult to identify, adding to the suspicion that they are likely to be merely local races. All are shoaling fish like the dace, rarely growing over 25 centimetres (just under 10 inches). The following species are noted:

- *Leuciscus svallize* (Heckel & Kner) from Dalmatia and southern Albania, which has 48-49 scales along the lateral line and 13 rays in the anal fin.

- *Leuciscus illyricus* (Heckel & Kner) has 49-54 scales along the lateral line and a body that is rather high and compressed.

- *Leuciscus ukliva* (Heckel) has a curved snout, 62-64 scales along the lateral line, and a faint dark, longitudinal band.

- *Leuciscus turskyi* (Heckel) has 70-72 scales along the lateral line and a broad, dark, longitudinal band across the body.

- *Leuciscus microlepis* (Heckel) has 73-75 scales along the lateral line and sometimes has a dark, longitudinal band across the body.

There is, however, a great deal of uncertainty about this classification, with the international fish classification database www.fishbase.org (accessed November 2010) placing these species not in the genus *Leuciscus* but spreading them into either *Telestes or Squalius*. Other scientists consider all of these various dace 'species' to be variations on the common dace, *Leuciscus leuciscus*.

In taxonomy, there are always 'shades of grey' in determining the distinction between closely-related species and subspecies, at least until adequate research has been conducted to verify the facts. Nevertheless, the sub-species *Leuciscus leuciscus burdigalensis* Valenciennes, 1844, is recognised in southern French rivers.

American 'Dace'

A range of cyprinid species encountered in North America are also referred to as 'dace'. These are also cyprinid fishes (the minnow and carp family) of the genera *Rhinichthys* and *Phoxinus* (the latter being the same genus as the familiar British/European minnow). These American species have at least superficial similarities with our own familiar European dace, so it is hardly surprising that European settlers should give them familiar European names. (The same is, after all, true of many of their regions, cities, states, trees, birds, etc.) These fish include:

- Blacknose dace: *Rhinichthys atratulus* (Hermann, 1804).

- Longnose dace: *Rhinichthys cataractae* (Valenciennes, 1842), of which there are several know subspecies.

- Las Vegas Dace: *Rhinichthys deaconi* Miller, 1984.

- Umpqua dace: *Rhinichthys evermanni* Snyder, 1908.

- Leopard dace: *Rhinichthys falcatus* (Eigenmann & Eigenmann, 1893).

- Western blacknose dace: *Rhinichthys meleagris* Agassiz, 1854.

- Speckled dace: *Rhinichthys nubilus* (Girard, 1856).

- Umatilla dace: *Rhinichthys umatilla* (Gilbert & Evermann, 1894).

- Mountain redbelly dace: *Phoxinus oreas.*

- Redbelly dace, or Northern redbelly dace: *Phoxinus eos.*

- Southern redbelly dace: *Phoxinus erythrogaster.*

Since all American 'dace' species appear capable of surviving in the UK, and some may have been introduced into our waters either accidentally or incidentally through the aquatic trade, there is now a legal restriction on the import and keeping in the UK of most species under the *Import of Live Fish (England and Wales) Act 1980,* or ILFA for short, supported by various orders implementing specific additional restrictions and mirrored by equivalent regulations in Scotland.

Dace ecology

Throughout evolutionary history, species have arisen and then either gone extinct or developed their forms and lifestyles to adapt to changing environmental conditions. We live today with a bewildering array of creatures, plants and microbes, all intimately and inextricably adapted to the place and other life forms with which they find themselves. The study of ecology looks at the relationship of organisms with their environment. The study of dace ecology can therefore reveal much about the fish and its modes of life as everything about this fish is honed by the master craftsman, Mother Nature, through millennia of evolutionary adaptation. Understanding how dace go about the daily dramas of survival, feeding and reproduction is the key to understanding how a fish, or indeed any other living thing, will respond. This is the science of ecology.

Preferred habitat

Look at the profile of a dace and compare it with that of a trout. Give or take the adipose fin, square tail, larger mouth and teeth of the trout, they are surprisingly similar. Nature is a wonderful architect, the process of billions of years of evolution adapting form to function perfectly. So the similarities and differences between trout and dace give us important clues as to their respective ecological niches.

Comparative profiles of dace and wild brown trout.

Both species are clearly adapted for a life in flowing water, a forward-pointing mouth enabling them to exploit food on the surface, mid-water or river bed. They are known as rheophilic (or 'current-loving') fish, most closely-associated with streams and rivers. By and large, they prefer river beds of gravel or sand, though at certain times of the year they have a preference for deeper waters where the bed type differs.

Dace are well-equipped for orientation in flowing water, possessing a high sensitivity to the rate and direction of their movements within a body of flowing water through sensing minute accelerations (inertial stimuli) via their labyrinth organs. Using these senses, dace are able to make compensatory movements against shifting water currents and thereby to maintain station within the river. This is the same adaptation that enables trout to act in a similar manner.

Stillwater dace

This is not to say that dace do not occur in stillwaters. Throughout their European range, Alwyne Wheeler notes in his 1969 book *The Fishes of Great Britain and North West Europe* that,

> *"The dace is typically a fish of clear, fairly fast-running streams and rivers, but is occasionally found in lakes and lowland rivers."*

Generally, these are either one of two types. Firstly, larger 'still' waters where wind, springs, inflowing streams and other forces actually create some surprising strong underwater currents, including for example Loch Lomond in Scotland which has a notable dace population today (albeit that dace are an introduced species in Scotland) including reputedly some very big individual specimens. Secondly, dace are sometimes to be found in stillwaters connected to streams, such as those formed from dams or else in parts of the southern counties where gravel extraction occurs. Here, dace might fall back into the stillwaters when streams are in spate, exploiting the static waters for some time and generally patrolling somewhere near the surface in small, tight shoals.

Writing in the 1993 book *A Passion for Angling,* Chris Yates describes the kind of stillwater that might be expected to hold dace yet the surprise at spotting them when unexpected,

> *"We had never seen stillwater dace before. But then we realized that the lake was not, in fact, ever quite still. Such was the strength of the feeder stream that there was a constant, just discernible flow down towards the outfall. However, the dace – fish of quick streams – still seemed a mystery."*

Dace are also to be found in some canals, particularly those with good river connections and sometimes strong flows. Examples of this include parts of the Exeter canal, the Kennet and Avon canal, and the Forth and Clyde canal.

Stillwaters are not, however, a typical nor prime habitat for dace. These fish are most at home in streamy water not dissimilar to that enjoyed by trout and chub.

Behaviour

Whereas trout tend to be territorial, the same can not be said of the dace. The dace is a shoaling species, very often gathering together in large numbers. This is particularly the case, often spectacularly so, during spawning when they can form great black shoals in faster waters over shallow gravels. Dace have a strong propensity to inhabit streamy waters, at least for most of the year. The exceptions to this are when they drop into slower-flowing waters to 'mend' from spawning and also during the cold months of winter when they avoid the strongest flows and the increased exposure of shallow waters when vegetation dies back.

Distribution

Dace have a wide geographic distribution across Europe. They are freely distributed throughout the rivers and streams of Europe north of the Pyrenees, though faring rather better in cooler countries. They do not occur in the Iberian, Italian or Greek peninsulas.

Dace are also widespread in small streams and larger rivers of England and Wales, though absent from the South West peninsula of England and western Wales. This inclination towards the south-east is due to the history of glaciation of the British Isles. The Reverend W. Houghton, in his classic and beautifully-illustrated 1879 book *British Fresh-Water Fishes* records that,

> *"In England the dace is found in many of our clear waters, but it is said not to occur in Ireland or Scotland."*

That, however, was then! Human introductions have seen dace spreading not merely in their English and Welsh range, but also locally into Ireland and parts of Scotland.

Some of these introductions are well-recorded, whilst others remain undocumented. Pete McParlin, for example, in an article in the magazine *Waterlog* in 2007, documents the return of fish to formerly polluted north eastern English rivers such as the Tyne, Wear and Tees beyond the Yorkshire Ouse which formerly marked the northernmost limit of many coarse fish species. The Wear fish appear to have been illicitly stocked into the recovering river by local anglers with fish from the Tweed to the north, itself stocked artificially and illegally rather than being naturally present. (An article by Derek Mills in Volume 50 of *Waterlog* records that the Tweed was found to hold a thriving dace population in the 1960s and 1970s, which may have resulted from salmon anglers releasing baits brought to the river to use in spinning mounts when salmon fishing.) Today, the Wear is a fine dace fishery and it is from the river in Durham that the current record fish was taken in August 2002 (a tale told in the chapter *Giant bags and whopping great dace*).

The glacial history of the British Isles means that dace are not native to the island of Ireland. The twelfth century writer Giraldus Cambrensis stated that there were no pike, perch, roach, gudgeon, minnow, tench and loach in Ireland and also observed that all the species known to him could live in salt water. This comprised primarily salmonid fishes. All seven of the salt-intolerant fish referred to by Giraldus have been introduced across Ireland over the last 400 years, often entailing multiple introductions. Tench, and perhaps also carp, were believed to have been introduced by continental monastic orders in late Medieval times.

The Earl of Cork is documented as introducing them in the seventeenth century. In his 1998 book *Ireland's Freshwaters*, Julian D. Reynolds charts both this history and that of the introduction of dace to Ireland. Both dace and roach were introduced into the Munster Blackwater in the nineteenth century, and they have prospered throughout that whole river system.

Roach, of course, have made a great success of spreading virtually right across the island, often by intent or accident at human hands. Dace, on the other hand, have been slower to find new waters. However, Reynolds records that dace spread through the Barrow system throughout the early 1990s. Parts of the Barrow catchment have diffuse links through bog streams with the huge River Shannon system to the north, and it is not impossible that dace (as indeed other fish and aquatic organisms) could cross over and exploit its flowing waters, particularly so in times of flood.

Furthermore, the headwaters of the Barrow rise very close to the main stem of the River Liffey, which flows eastwards to its estuary at Dublin. Ireland's Grand Canal also joins the Barrow, providing another avenue along which dace could conceivably spread across Ireland. We are probably in the early days of the colonisation of Ireland by dace. Their rapid spread from the established strongholds in the south west of the island is probably hampered by their preference for sharper flows and clean spawning gravels as compared to their cousins, the roach.

Mobility

Fish live in a medium some eight hundred times denser and sixty-five times more viscous than air. This creates a conflict. Buoyancy offers them the advantage of maintaining their depth in the water without great energy expenditure through the development of a swim bladder, a double-walled air-containing sac evolved as an outgrowth from the front of the gut. Buoyancy also averts the need for a heavy, weight-bearing skeleton. However, the greater viscosity of water also resists forward movement in a manner alien to us air-dwellers. Holding station in the flow is something achieved with certain adaptations and energy use.

To adapt them to faster flows, dace have an elongated, streamlined shape, a smooth, mucus-coated surface that markedly decreases the frictional resistance of water passing over the fish, and strong muscle blocks beneath the flanks to provide propulsive power. Fine control on orientation and movement is provided by both vertical fins – the dorsal, tail and anal fins – and paired fins – the pectoral and pelvic (or ventral) fins.

Another facet of the biology of the swimming apparatus of the dace is that the fins are positioned for continuous swimming, not for the explosive burst of an ambush predator like a pike.

Whilst the fins of an ambush predator like a pike (below) are positioned towards the rear of the body, like an outboard motor, those of the dace (above) are ideally positioned for continuous swimming.

Scientific studies of fish swimming speeds generally focus on two parameters. Firstly, there is the maximum sustained swimming speed, giving an impression of the kind of current to which a fish is best suited, and secondly a burst speed reflecting instantaneous acceleration. The SWIMIT model is one of a number of computer programmes which, based on known data, predicts these two values of swimming speed for several native UK fish species, adjusted for the size of the fish and water temperature. In the table below, values of the two swimming speeds (in centimetres per second) are calculated for water of 12°C based on theoretical fish of 15 centimetres and 30 centimetres in length. (The latter would be a very big dace!)

Fish species	Fish length in cm	Sustained swimming speed in cm/s	Burst swimming speed in cm/s
Dace	15 cm 30 cm	60cm/s 89cm/s	138cm/s 168cm/s
Bream	15 cm 30 cm	40cm/s 79cm/s	131cm/s 148cm/s
Brown trout	15 cm 30 cm	113cm/s 177cm/s	133cm/s 180cm/s
Barbel	15 cm 30 cm	62cm/s 80cm/s	223cm/s 264cm/s

There are a number of interesting aspects to these comparative swimming speeds. Dace are significantly quicker at sustained swimming than bream, as one might expect from knowledge of their streamlining and preferred habitat. They also rival, and sometimes exceed, barbel, though are not as comfortable in faster water as brown trout. However, unlike brown trout, dace can produce a proportionately greater explosive burst of speed over a short distance, albeit not in the same league as that of the barbel. So, overall, the dace is equipped for life in the same types of streamy water beloved of barbel though not quite as free-flowing as that which is ideal for brown trout, and they also have the cyprinid capacity to bolt away from danger or to surge through faster water when needed.

Habitat usage

The above information about swimming speeds has to be interpreted cautiously. This is not merely because they are extrapolations from a computer model, with all of the uncertainties that this brings with it. It is just that natural rivers, despite the worst excesses of some unsympathetic river engineering schemes up to the 1980s, are far from the smooth flowing channels in which laboratory data on swimming speeds are collected. The creation of diverse current speeds is one of the many important contributions of habitat in rivers.

Owing to frictional resistance, any hard surface in flowing water contains a thin film of relatively calm water close to its surface. It is in this thin film of less energetic flow that many invertebrates and fish fry live, their food brought to them by the currents though sheltered in their micro-habitat from high-energy flows which would result in far greater energy expenditure and risk of detachment and predation in the turbulent current. Adult fish too can make use of stiller zones in fast-flowing reaches of river. Their bodies may be far too big to allow them to exploit the 'boundary layer' over stones and the river bed. However, cobbles, boulders, dead wood and other larger obstructions produce turbulence, often betrayed by a 'boil' on the water's surface, effectively increasing the size of the 'boundary zone' within rivers and creating notable 'lies' to which fish are attracted. This is why you will see dace (and trout and other fish) holding station at a particular point in a seemingly featureless run of water; it contains the optimal balance of flow and shelter, and a constant 'conveyor belt' of food items in the adjacent stronger currents.

Various authorities have classified the 'zones' of rivers. One of the better-known of these is Marcel Huet's classification of European river zones from the 1950s, which identified:

Current speed	Zone descriptor	Other features
> 90 cm s-1	Fishless	Too turbulent for fish
> 60 cm s-1	Trout Zone	Trout with bullheads, minnows and stone loach
> 20 cm s-1	Grayling Zone	Grayling and faster-water species including dace, gudgeon and bleak
> 10 cm s-1	Barbel Zone	Barbel typifying moderate currents shared with fish such as chub, dace and bleak
< 10 cm s-1	Bream Zone	Dominated by shoals of bream and other deeper-bodied fish, including smaller species such as gudgeon and bleak

This is, of course, a synthetic classification, with rivers acting more as a continuum between 'zone types'. Indeed, some zones may be missing in some rivers, for example the absence of a bream zone in a fast river that reaches its estuary with little or no floodplain. However, the 'zone' classification does serve to illustrate the kinds of current speeds favoured by different fish communities and other elements of the ecosystem. Typically, dace can share faster waters with trout and grayling, but can also prosper in more moderate flows which they share with chub.

To a significant extent, and allied to water quality and flows, habitat quality establishes the 'carrying capacity' for fish in a stream. As Nick Giles describes for trout habitat exploitation, in his 2005 book *The Nature of Trout,*

"The 'dead spot' behind the rock where current speeds are slow and variable and where food items tend to be deposited is an easy feeding lie. Just upstream is an area where the current pushes hard against the rock and is held back, forming a 'cushion'. This, too, is a good efficient lie for trout to occupy. Like the March Brown nymph, trout occupying rocky glides have a wealth of potential shelter offering productive feeding areas."

The same principle applies absolutely to dace, a fish adapted to a similar type of existence in streamy water, albeit water not quite as rapid as the upper limits of flow rate in which trout may prosper.

We must also recall that, no matter how high its quality, no single habitat type supports the needs of dace and other fish throughout the year and across all their various life stages. As we have already observed, there are times of year when dace require deeper and steadier water, as well as shallow, vegetated runs in which to spawn and to act as nursery areas for fry.

They even make extensive use of tributary streams, channels and backwaters connected to the river. If it is to be optimal for dace, these too have to feature as part of the mix of habitats making up a river reach. Habitat diversity is of critical importance, and is an issue to which we will return later in this book. Suffice to say that sensitive river management can significantly increase the effective 'carrying capacity' of both fish and the broader ecosystem of which they are a balanced part, not to mention aiding predator evasion and helping winter survival during periods of high flow.

Migration

All fish migrate. It is often wrongly supposed, by both amateur observers and some professional river managers alike, that there is some fundamental distinction in the tendency to migrate between the salmonid fishes and their coarse counterparts. Such assumptions are misplaced.

Dace will make free use of tributary streams, however small, as part of their active movement around river systems.

The salmon, sea trout, brown trout and other fish with adipose fins and silver flanks are well-known for their dynamic life histories, utilising different reaches of river, some also the open sea, throughout life. For these fishes, it is essential to maintain the natural connection of flowing water from tiny headstreams to montane torrents, piedmond flats, the more genteel depths of lowland rivers and their merging with coastal seas. However, it is only far more recently that fishery scientists and the managers who use their research have come to recognise and gradually accept that the cyprinids and other coarse fish in a river system also have a dynamic existence. Not only do they actively move across from the mid-channel to outlying channels and floodplains, but they also rove often significant distances both up and down rivers. This they may do on daily, annual and other cycles.

Of all the coarse species, the migrations of dace are perhaps the best studied. A large part of the reason for this is that they were abundant in the stretch of the River Piddle traversing the Freshwater Biological Association's river laboratory at East Stoke, Dorset, where much of the pioneering work on radio-tracking of coarse fish was undertaken in the UK. The well-respected fish biologist Dr Mike Ladle and his research team pioneered the application of radio-telemetry methods to track dace which had been fitted painlessly with micro transponder tags. Their published research forms the basis for the discussion in this chapter backed up by my conversations with Mike himself.

In the early 1990s, preliminary tracking results showed that dace are a highly mobile species, capable of extensive, often rapid migrations both up and down the river. All of the tagged dace demonstrated the same tendency to remain at selected sites for extended periods then suddenly to relocate rapidly within the river. The research team was able to demonstrate that dace utilised clearly-defined daytime and night-time habitats. Frequent and often rapid returns by individual dace to locations that they had previously occupied at dawn and dusk suggest a strong linkage between habitat use and light intensity. This behaviour has remarkable parallels with roosting behaviour in birds.

The team also found that recently-spawned dace, captured, radio-tagged and released on known spawning sites, maintained their shoaling behaviour with other untagged dace, but that in this 'mending' phase these fish occupied slow-flowing shaded sites, often in the deepest and slowest-flowing reaches out of the main river channel. This is not 'typical' habitat for dace at other times of the year, their preference for freshwater flows being well-documented, so conservation of energy for recovery from spawning may be a crucial causative factor.

Dace inhabiting brackish water tend to make spawning migrations into the fresh waters of coastal streams. Such behaviour is know from the lower-salinity regions of the upper Baltic Sea, as well as up the Hampshire Avon and Stour rivers that merge at Christchurch Harbour. The same upstream spawning migrations from brackish waters are also observed in other freshwater species such as pike, perch, roach and ide. Like salmonids, these coarse fish too tend to return to their home-stream every year as adults.

The same is observed where these dace inhabit still waters. In some large northern Finnish lakes, dace and other fish are known to migrate in and out of lakes, either up into inflowing streams of down into outflowing rivers, for spawning.

The underlying lesson here is that we have to manage obstructions to fish movements very carefully if we are not to harm the recruitment and wellbeing of dace stocks, and indeed those of other fishes. Until the 1990s, for example, Carlisle Weir on the River Eden in Cumbria was well-known as a place where dense shoals of dace would form prior to spawning. For these fish, the weir presented a largely impassable barrier to spawning migrations in anything other than the highest river levels. Once a fish pass was installed on the weir during the 1990s, these dace, as well as trout, salmon and other species, were able to make their continued journey upstream in far greater numbers, with beneficial outcomes for fish stocks in the whole river system. Similar principles apply to many other rivers, where obstructions to access tributary streams have been removed. Dace are mobile creatures, actively using a matrix of habitat types in a river section; we have to guard against reducing that habitat diversity or denying them access to it.

Population trends

Dace were once very common across their natural range in the UK. However, dace today, and large dace in particular, are generally perceived by anglers as becoming increasingly scarce. Hard evidence to substantiate this perception is elusive. However, the slowing of river flows through over-abstraction of water, siltation of spawning gravels by poor agricultural practices, and increased predation from cormorants and otters are all advanced as explanations.

The rise in cormorant populations and their colonisation of inland stillwaters, rivers and streams is very commonly blamed for the demise of many coarse and game fisheries. There is certainly compelling evidence of the detrimental effects of heavy cormorant predation on small and vulnerable waters. However, I for one am wary of laying all blame on one single cause. Folks like me spent a lot of the late 1970s and the 1980s, and depressingly some of the early 1990s too, arguing that pike were not bad for fisheries just because they ate fish; a common prejudice then leveled by many gamekeepers, fishery managers, match-fishing club committees and angling writers as a reason for seeking to eradicate them. Today, we know better, and most people accept that a balanced ecosystem can support predatory fish which, left unmanaged, will in any case tend to limit their own populations. Sadly, the same bigotry is often transferred to cormorants today, when the causes are often far more complex.

As I look out over the upper Bristol Avon as I write, a stretch of river where the cormorants can be a local nuisance but are generally castigated as an evil along the whole catchment, I see also a river suffering from severe low flows due to over-abstraction of groundwater, marginal trampling (poaching) and denudation of emergent vegetation by stock, sediment inputs from intensive and poorly-managed farming interests, nutrient enrichment from sewage and farming practices, a history of flood management that has decimated natural habitat diversity, and a host of other factors that collectively place a stranglehold on the river ecosystem. Add an influx of cormorants during a cold winter and we have the proverbial 'straw that breaks the camel's back'.

But do we blame that single 'straw', or do we seek to be strategic in addressing the multiplicity of impacts that mean that the river ecosystem can not sustain the additional predation? Where I sometimes fish for dace on the tidal River Exe in Devon, the stocks of silver fish are huge, as are those of the cormorants that perch in great numbers on the pylons running along the river! The pro- and con-cormorant debate is deeply entrenched, and I know I will not change anyone's preconceived ideas. However, perhaps I can at least seed some broader thoughts in the minds of those not yet committed to either trench; we need to restore the health of our rivers first to enable them to produce and protect more of their native fish, rather than pointing an accusing finger on predators feeding on the fewer, more vulnerable fish that they contain today.

Elsewhere across the European range of the dace, populations have been spread by human interference. However, perhaps the low value of the dace as a food fish, its higher oxygen demands relative to other coarse fish that can be transported as pike baits, and the requirements of the fish for stronger flows and clean spawning gravels means that humans have less interest in the deliberate translocation of dace than they do in the case of, say, the ruffe or the roach?

The senses of dace

Dace are equipped with a broad array of senses akin to most other cyprinid fishes, though these are tuned to their particular active life habits. These senses are hard for us humans to envisage, based as we on land and in air and not immersed and buoyed up by a dense medium of surrounding water. Also unlike dace, we don't taste (and/or smell) with the whole of our body surface, detecting fine concentrations of substances around us, and even finer gradients within our surrounding medium to give us a three-dimensional sense of what is where.

Neither is much of the surface of our bodies acute to fine pressure changes in our surrounding medium, building a three-dimensional image of the movement of water against other objects and creatures. We see, yes, though through clear air and not murky water. On the back pages of some magazines, we see occasional adverts for pheromones – inter-person chemical stimuli most often advertised as sexual attractants – yet for dace and other fish bathed in the dense medium of water, communication by hormones external to the body is commonplace rather than something about which scientists remain uncertain.

All in all, life feels quite different to a human than it does to a dace. We have to be wary of trying to generalise what we know of the senses of a dace to fit our own descriptions and sensations; to do so would be to overlook their extraordinary nature and the implications for those who might try to deceive dace with a baited hook.

The visual sense

Water, murky water in particular, conducts light only poorly compared to air. Unlike many sight-hunting predatory fish (such as pike), the eyes of a dace are not proportionately large compared to body size, and neither are they comparatively small like those of fish relying predominantly upon chemical senses (such as tench or catfish). Rather, they are more or less in proportion to the eyes of most other cyprinid fishes, such as roach and barbel, indicating a generalist lifestyle in which sight plays a part in a suite of other senses.

The pike, a visual hunter, has large eyes whereas the tench, which relies mainly upon its chemical senses, has proportionally smaller eyes. Though relative eye size in fish varies with age, those of the dace are intermediate indicating their role in a generalist suite of senses.

However, we know from watching dace, as they feed on drifting matter in shallow running water, that their vision is extremely acute. Only for the fry of dace are the eyes disproportionately large, again a common feature amongst cyprinid fishes, helping the young fish visually locate small invertebrate food more effectively. Eye growth slows down as the fish age and the diet includes more vegetation and other matter. As in all cyprinid fishes, vision is in full colour enabled by well developed cones in the retina (the light receptor in the back of the eyes).

The chemical senses

Fully immersed as they are in the dense medium of water, which not only carries many dissolved substances but also prevents the drying of the skin, chemical sense organs are distributed across the entire outer surface of dace. These organs are at their most dense around the head and forward parts of the body, but they do cover the whole outer surface of the fish including in the mouth and gill rakers. There is, in practice, little or no distinction between the senses of smell and taste for a dace, the whole forming a 'general chemical sense'.

We also know that dace are able to detect fine differences in the concentration of various dissolved substances across their bodies. This provides them with a three-dimensional sense of the chemical environment in which they swim; this is particularly hard for a human to envisage. There are, however, dedicated nostrils on the snout, each comprising a flap of skin over a short olfactory groove containing a 'mucosal rosette' coated in many sensory cells.

Fish are not only sensitive to various chemical substances, but also to pheromones – hormone substances emitted outside the body – which play various roles in communication between fish and within shoals. Such hormonal communication between dace can become particularly significant in murky water when sight is compromised. There is also evidence that dace and other prey fishes can detect pheromones released by predatory fish, as well as 'fright substances' produced under stress by their own kind.

The physical senses

Water is an efficient medium for the transfer of pressure waves, so it is no surprise to discover that dace and other fishes have elaborate systems to detect pressure waves. In part, this includes a sense that we might equate to hearing, though this extends into far lower frequencies than are detectable by the human ear and also far more minute sounds than we can hear. Hearing occurs in an inner ear, and this is connected to the swim bladder which, being gas-filled, is effective at amplifying underwater sound. However, water pressure waves are also picked up by the lateral line system, found in virtually all cyprinids, which comprises a line of canals along the flanks containing groups of hair-like sensory cells. Their pressure-sensing systems enable dace to detect a three-dimensional world of currents, movements and 'sound' reflections.

This is supported by a familiar (to us) sense of touch. Touch is particularly important in shoaling and spawning behaviour, with the tubercles formed on the body surface of a male dace in spawning livery believed to be an important stimulant for female fish to release their eggs.

As addressed previously, the labyrinth organ of a dace is also finely attuned to minute accelerations (inertial stimuli), which give the fish a high sensitivity to the rate and direction of their movements in flowing water. There is evidence also that dace are sensitive to pressure via stretch receptors within their bodies, particularly around the deformable swim bladder, and that they also detect changes in temperature as well as perhaps electrical and magnetic stimuli.

Reproduction and growth

For dace, as all fish, survival through to breeding and the associated passing of genes to future generations is the underpinning principle governing their entire lives. Diverse reproductive strategies are employed by the many species of fishes, some dropping live young, others guarding their immobile eggs or nurturing the vulnerable fry. However, the general pattern of reproduction amongst the cyprinids is one of shoal spawning, scattering a large number of eggs to which are extended no subsequent parental care. This *high-fecundity* strategy entails the deposition of many eggs in optimal habitat but, beyond that, the eggs, hatchlings and fry depend upon chance to evade the onslaught of predators and disease.

Preparation for spawning

Being one of the first coarse fish to spawn in the year, dace 'mend' quickly in the spring, often entailing a period of retreat into deeper and slacker areas of a river immediately after the spawning act. However, from late spring through summer, they show a strong preference for streamier and often shallow waters in which they feed freely to build condition and develop roe for the following season. As autumn sets in, dace may relocate into deeper water where there are reasonable flows of water. Here, throughout the winter, their bodies, particularly those of female fish, become distended by the swelling reproductive organs. These changes, hormonally-driven, can lead to late-winter dace feeding intensively when the opportunity allows.

By late winter, both male and female fish broaden in girth. However, it is the female fish that become most distended by their burden of eggs, developing a deep body with a pronounced 'pigeon chest' as the ovaries expand to their full size. At this time, as much as 19% of the body weight of a female dace can be accounted for by its roe. This represents a very significant investment of the annual energy budget of a female dace into the next generation. (By contrast,

15% of the body weight of a female roach may be accounted for by spawn.) The body of a gravid female dace also takes on a brighter silvery-white coloration, and becomes soft to the touch like a fat herring.

Male dace also change in profile, though this is far from as exaggerated as that of the female. Instead, the body of the male often takes on a more bronze coloration and he becomes rough to the touch due to a covering of fine tubercles which, though more concentrated around the head, are distributed right across the body. The male fish also shed mucus, enhancing the roughness of the body. It is generally assumed that this extra roughness helps male fish 'stick' for longer to the sides of female fish as they simultaneously release their roe and milt (or sperm), and it may also stimulate her to release her eggs on contact during spawning.

Spawning

As previously discussed, dace shoals may travel several miles to reach ideal spawning habitat. In the days prior to the act of spawning, sometimes a fortnight or so, thousands of dace may gather at certain times of the day in great black shoals over generally well-known spawning sites in shallow streamy water.

Dace are the earliest coarse fish species to spawn in the UK, taking place anything from February to (exceptionally) June. Spawning occurs in the latter part of the night or at first light. It has even been observed on occasions taking place when there was frost on the river banks. Dace are adapted to cooler waters, spawning in advance of their competitors. This enables them to utilise a longer period of the growing season before the fry have to brave winter floods, a time when body size and strength are of crucial importance. The triggers for spawning are primarily hormonal, governed predominantly by day length, though this is modified by local factors such as temperature and flow conditions.

In their somewhat dated but still authoritative 1980 book *Water Quality Criteria for Freshwater Fish*, J.S. Alabaster and R. Lloyd review the scientific literature addressing observed spawning temperatures for a range of fish, noting that dace most generally were found spawning in water of 5-9°C, whereas the predominant temperate ranges for other fish with which dace could conceivably cross-breed included bleak at 17-28°C, roach at 8-19.4°C and chub at a suspiciously precise 18.4°C. The only other leuciscine species with a strongly overlapping spawning temperature was the ide at 4-15°C. Gudgeon, not a leuciscine species but typical of many other British members of the carp family, generally spawn in water near 12°C.

The prime months for the spawning act are between March and May, depending upon latitude, climate and the clemency of the preceding winter. In the UK, spawning is generally earlier in warmer southern localities as compared to the north of its range. I have certainly seen dace spawning in the end of February on the Hampshire Avon, a chalk river warmed significantly by groundwater influxes from the underlying chalk strata which enter the river at 10-11°C. These both warm the river in winter and cool it in summer. A severe cold winter or a 'late' spring can delay spawning until as late as May, or exceptionally June.

Spawning takes place in gravelly shallows, usually at night and after a short up-stream migration. The females arrive at the spawning site and stay in its vicinity until spent; the males mostly move upstream in the evening and return to deeper water after dawn. There is only one spawning per fish per year. The largest fish spawn earliest in the season; the most recently matured fish do so last. The time span over which all such year classes of dace phase their spawning can be as much as a month. Sometimes, two distinct though close spawning periods may be observed in dace populations, usually attributed to the extended spawning period early in the year being interrupted temporarily by cold weather.

Spawning follows the typical shoal scatter-spawning of cyprinid fishes, with the eggs fertilised by clouds of milt released by male fish. Favoured spawning habitat is rapid water over gravel with a typical particle diameter of 10-40mm diameter in water of 9-10°C. Females, jostled by ardent male fish, release their eggs to be fertilised by the milt of their suitors. A 20 centimetre female dace may release 6,500 to 9,500 eggs, though as few as 3,000 and as many as 27,000 eggs have been known. The number of eggs is related to the size of the female fish.

The eggs are pale yellow or orange in colour, each 1.5-2 millimetres in diameter and with a sticky outer surface. These eggs are somewhat larger than those of chub and roach, which typically measure 0.7-1.2 and 1.0-1.5 millimetres in diameter respectively. This may help the young dace grow strongly when food is otherwise sparse in the cool late winter or early spring river. The eggs fall in the water column, attaching to stones and gravel, and sometimes also to submerged vegetation.

Once fish have spawned, they may remain a while on the spawning shingles, but they will then tend to drop back into deeper, calmer water to 'mend' after their exertions. Once the adult fish have recovered, they may again relocate to the streamy waters, to which they are so admirably adapted, to feed strongly throughout the spring and summer. The reproductive organs begin to develop again even at this stage, in preparation for their investment in the coming season.

Hatching and development

Hatching is slow due to the preference for spawning in cooler conditions. During this time, the eggs are immobile and vulnerable to predation or attack by other fish, insects, fungi and just about any opportunist and predatory organisms in the water. Once adhering to a suitable underwater surface, be that rocks, gravel or plants, the eggs remain firmly attached; scientific studies suggest that only some 2% of dace eggs may be lost when a flood follows spawning. The earliness of spawning in the year in cooler waters, and the vulnerability of potential egg-raiders to their own predators in shallow water, go some way to offsetting losses relative to the eggs of those fish which spawn later in the year. In a study of dace in Dorset's River Frome published in 1980, the biologist Chris Mills estimated egg survival from spawning to hatching to be between 8-22%. There is a close relationship between the percentage of surviving eggs and substrate composition where poor survival occurs in areas of the river bed with high silt and low gravel content.

The eggs hatch in twenty-five days at a temperature of 13°C (55°F). From each emerges an alevin, 7.5-9.5 millimetres long and still attached to a yolk sac, which it continues to absorb for a day or two before becoming free-swimming. Since they are incompletely developed on hatching, this alevin stage is also referred to as a 'free embryo'. Alevins lack distinct fins, possessing delicate fin-folds around the dorsal and ventral flanks and tail. Unlike those of some other fishes, the alevins of dace and other cyprinids do not have the capacity to stick to surfaces and so depend for survival upon shelter from currents. Appropriate habitat diversity is therefore critical to dace survival at this stage.

A week after hatching, the alevins have metamorphosed into fry which become free-swimming, attaining a length of around 8.0-9.5 millimetres and around 3.5 milligrammes in (wet) weight. At this stage, there is no fin differentiation, the fins gradually becoming more distinct and the rays appearing and extending over the first weeks of life. The larvae of different coarse fish are notoriously difficult to tell apart though, for those brave enough to try, Adrian Pinder's *Keys to larval and juvenile stages of coarse fishes from fresh waters in the British Isles* is, like most of the excellent series of Freshwater Biological Association keys, a definitive work. One of the characteristic features of larval dace is that their dorsal pigmentation includes two lines of closely-spaced, solid melanophores (brown/black pigment-containing cells).

The diet of 0+ dace (those in their first year of life) has been studied on the River Dee where it was found that, during development, dace fed on a sequence of food types. Initially, the dace fry were mainly carnivorous, feeding on a variety of invertebrate food, later becoming nocturnally carnivorous and diurnally omnivorous. 0+ roach fry showed a similar pattern, although after the first two months of life they were more herbivorous and detritivorous (eating amorphous organic matter) than dace. Good habitat supporting diverse food types is therefore essential for survival and good growth rates for the fry of both species of fish.

By six weeks old, the young dace have attained a length of around 20 millimetres and around 77 milligrammes in (wet) weight. By ten weeks old, they reach around 30 millimetres and around 254 milligrammes, and by fourteen weeks they attain around 38 millimetres and around half a gramme in weight.

'Young of year' dace taken from the River Wye in November 2006.

Growth and mortality

Fry growth continues quickly, with dace growth slowed to a lesser extent during the winter compared to roach and chub. The young at one year measure 6-7 centimetres in length, averaging around 15 centimetres by the end of their second year, 18 centimetres by the end of their third year, 20 centimetres after four years and 22 centimetres by the end of their sixth year.

As for other cyprinid fishes, ageing of dace is most readily achieved by examining scale samples taken from the flank of the fish. The growth of each bony scale is discontinuous, with the formation of an annulus, or concentric 'growth ring', which signals the end of each year's growth. By counting the number of annuli, cross-checked with other scales, the age of the fish can be determined as one does the age of a tree. A fish with one annulus is described as a '1+'. A fish that has attained two completed growth seasons with two corresponding annuli is '2+', and so on.

Their affinity with cool water enables dace to grow even at temperatures as low as 8°C; this adaptation enables them to thrive in the cool rivers and brackish coastal seas of Scandinavia. Due to this adaptation to cool water, dace tend to grow on a more continuous basis throughout the seasons than do many cyprinid fish, with the result that the annuli on their scales are far less distinct than, say, those of a chub or roach.

A small minority of dace, both female and male, may mature sexually and spawn when only a year old. However, many more fish mature and spawn in their second year, and later in more nutrient-poor waters. Nick Giles, in his 1994 *Freshwater Fishes of the British Isles: A Guide for Anglers and Naturalists*, records that female dace from Dorset's River Frome mature at 2-5 years, with more usually doing so at 3-4 years, spawning then each year until their maximum age of 10 or 11 years. Maturity at 3-4 years old has also been observed as the norm on the River Wye catchment in mid-Wales. The growth rate of male fish is generally faster than that of females, perhaps related to the higher proportion of annual productivity invested in reproductive organs by female fish.

Mortality and longevity

Mortality in younger fish is extremely high, as befits their role in riverine food chains. Loss of dace from year classes continues as they age, resulting in a classic population structure comprising many younger fish and few older specimens. The 0+ (first year of life) component represents over half of the production (conversion of food matter to biomass) of the whole dace population in rivers.

Dace rarely exceed 25 centimetres in length and 200 grammes in weight, although there are a few authentic records of specimens exceeding 30 centimetres. They are said to be one of the shorter-lived coarse fishes. Longevity is said to vary with the richness of the environment: dace may attain seven or eight years in rich environments where they grow quickly, but may potentially reaching eleven or more years where they grow slowly in poorer environments. In any water, a ten-year-old dace is a venerable fish.

J.M. Hellawell's studies in the early 1970s of populations of dace in two tributaries of the River Wye, the main stem of which rises in mid-Wales and then flows into

England to enter the sea in the Bristol Channel, has revealed sex ratio changes with age. The gender ratio is more or less 1:1 for younger fish, but there is a preponderance of females with increasing age. This is largely explaining by differential mortality, with females commonly attaining 10-11 years but few male dace reaching 8 years.

Not all spawning years are as strongly represented in dace populations within a river. This may reflect poor spawning conditions, severe floods the following year flushing out the vulnerable fry, a shortage of food, a pollution event, or a host of other factors. Some years, there are strong 'year classes' which can dominate the dace population. Whilst this is normal, and great fun for the angler as the year class ages, a balance between year classes, obviously with more younger fish and smaller numbers of ageing fish due to normal mortality, is most reflective of a balanced fishery ecosystem. This inter-annual variability can be quite marked for species such as chub, which are more comfortable in warmer waters, but the adaptation of dace to early spawning means that there is more frequent recruitment, and consequently more even age distributions in the population compared to other cyprinids.

Food and Feeding

As we have observed from their form, dace share with trout at least some adaptations to feeding on drift brought to them by the river's current. However, they also move around a great deal in rivers, both on a seasonal and daily cycle, exploiting a range of different habitat types and also the varied food items that occur there. The diet of a dace is then not uniform but varies over time.

They are keen feeders in most seasons, even sometimes when there is snow on the ground and frost in the trees. In fact, their adaptation to cooler rivers means that they need to feed quite intensely throughout the winter to build up reserves of energy and nutrients ready for spawning early in the season. Dace are also eager to feed in the warmer months, often seen dimpling the surface for floating food and as readily intercepting submerged items carried to them on the current or else active on the river bed.

The principal food items of dace

Scientific research has shown that the young of dace prey upon a sequence of food items in the wild. One of the most fascinating pieces of research on the diet of the juveniles (0+ fish) of dace and roach was undertaken by one of my scientific colleagues, Dr Neil Weatherley, as part of his PhD research on the River Dee in the early 1980s. Information on the dietary composition of young dace derives from Neil's published papers and from conversations we have had, augmented by additional research reviewed from a variety of published sources.

Upon becoming free-swimming, the fry of dace are mainly carnivorous, feeding almost exclusively on microscopic rotifers (the *Rotifera* or 'wheel animalcules') for the first three weeks of life. By their fourth week, the juvenile dace are able to progress to the slightly larger nauplii larvae of water fleas (cladocerans and copepods) and also to take diatoms (unicellular brown algae). By their fifth week of life, when the young dace have attained a length of some 16 millimetres, they can progress to a more varied diet that also begins to include aerial insects, the aquatic larvae of chironomids (bloodworms) as well as tubificids (fine worms).

This animal-rich diet of juvenile dace, and indeed many other species of fish, serves an additional essential purpose. Upon hatching, the gut of the dace is relatively undeveloped, comprising simply a straight tube from mouth to anus with no differentiated areas. It does not even develop a loop, extending its effective length, until about six weeks after hatching. Therefore, fish fry below this age depend upon the digestive enzymes of their prey items, released from the invertebrates' guts when they are swallowed and masticated, to break down food that the fish have ingested.

By the time they reach nine or ten weeks old, dace larvae are able to ingest algae and detritus (amorphous organic matter often comprising primarily decomposing plant matter rich in bacteria and other micro-organisms). The diet is dominated by blue-green algae and detritus by the age of three months. There is some evidence that this shift to a more vegetarian diet is imposed by limitation of animal food in the river edges favoured by the young fish, particularly so on the River Dee which was believed to be food limited at the time of Weatherley's research. However, young dace were also found to migrate from the littoral zone of the river into open water by night to feed on suspended plankton, maximising food availability when their own predators were feeding less effectively.

Throughout their early life, dace feed on a near-continuous basis with prey changing radically with time of day and, in all probability, food availability. They feed predominantly upon aerial insects by day and through until after sunset, reverting to a more omnivorous, opportunist habit after dark. By contrast, roach fry share the same diet for the first two months, but then move more quickly and permanently to a herbivorous/detritivorous diet.

Throughout the winter, the young dace shift again, feeding primarily upon insects, their larvae and other aquatic invertebrates. This may reflect the availability of food, although at this time of year roach will eat more detritus and other plant matter.

Whereas roach have an appetite for detritus, the different habitat use by dace seems to sway them away from this as a predominant food source. However, as cyprinids with some specific adaptations to sharper flows though many also to a more generalist, omnivorous life style, it is likely that dace will freely accept detritus when other food sources are sparse. In later life, dace will also continue to consume significant amounts of algae and higher plants. The seeds of terrestrial vegetation falling into the water can also be eagerly taken by dace, either picked from the current or from the bed of the river.

Insects comprise the most important of the animal foods consumed by larger and adult dace. This comprises principally the aquatic larvae of caddis flies (*Trichopterans*), the larvae and adults of non-biting midges (*chironomids*) and of black-flies (*Simulium*) as well as terrestrial insects and flying aquatic insects when they are on the wing during the summer months.

Caddis larvae, these with cases built from sticks, are a major part of the diet of adult dace.

Aside from this seasonal harvest, the various groups of benthic (bottom-dwelling) aquatic invertebrates that occur in rivers all year round are important elements of the diet of dace, particularly in winter when other forms are less active or conspicuous. These invertebrates include molluscs (small aquatic snails and mussels), leeches and crustaceans (mainly gammarid shrimps and the water-slater *Asellus*), as well as any larval stages of insects that remain active.

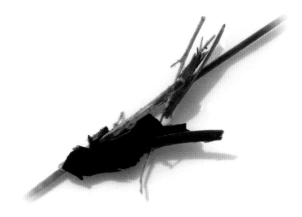

The larvae of these two different caddis species build their cases from dead leaves and grass stems and from freshly cut vegetation respectively.

Dace will readily accept invertebrate food such as small water snails (this is a species of Hydrobia), larvae of up-winged flies (ephemeropterans) and freshwater shrimps; particularly so during the winter when other food is scarce.

In addition to these aquatic life-forms, dace will gladly feast upon terrestrial organisms washed into rivers, including drowned flies, other insects and their larvae, small terrestrial snails and slugs and worms falling into the water, and so forth. In fact, pretty much any food item of suitable size and availability may be gladly accepted by dace.

This includes the fry of other species of fish, as well as the larvae of amphibians. As we will explore later in this book, the piscivorous (fish-eating) habits of dace may be overlooked in terms of their importance both to the fish and to the would-be angler.

Timing of feeding

As we have seen, dace are one of our more mobile freshwater fishes, with pronounced daily and seasonal migration habits. This, of course, affects feeding, and indeed may be driven largely by the conflicting needs of feeding and evading predators as well as preparation for spawning.

Often, dace will spend a large part of the day resting up in open glides of water evading their predators, though they will more often than not gladly intercept any nutritious offering arriving on the current. As dusk approaches, the dace then tend to move upstream into shallow gravel runs and riffles. They would be vulnerable to predators, particularly aerial predators, in these shallows by day, but the safety of half-light or darkness enables them to graze relatively unimpeded upon the rich invertebrate communities found there. In particular, the large numbers of caddis fly larvae that can be found drifting downstream at dusk, or else moving more confidently on the river bed or vegetation in the half-light, form a major component of the diet of dace. The peaks of feeding are crepuscular, taking place at dawn and dusk, though dace may continue to feed on these invertebrates throughout the night. Where food sources are sparse, dace will often be forced into a more continuous pattern of feeding.

Further scientific research has established that caddis larvae become an increasingly important element of the diet as dace grow larger and better able to tackle the relatively large and nutritious larvae. There is also an observed bias towards vegetation in the diet in the summer and the consumption of animals in the winter. To a large extent, this may reflect the availability of food with season.

Since the gut of the dace, as indeed most cyprinid fishes, is a relatively simple looped tube, lacking a stomach to store food, dace do need to eat on a near-continuous basis. As cold-blooded (poikilothermic or ectothermic) creatures, whose body temperature varies with that of their surroundings, the metabolic rate and hence the feeding rate of dace is governed significantly by the temperature of the surrounding river water. Other physiological signals also affect hunger, particularly the demands upon the fish as they prepare for spawning early in the year.

Conversely, hunger can be significantly or completely suppressed by danger, including the presence of predators such as disturbance from a clumsy angler, or other environmental stresses such as pollution. At these times of stress, the instincts of dace turn to evasion rather than consumption.

Predators of dace

In nature, being eaten is as natural as eating. Predators are as integral a part of the natural cycle as plants and insects. Aquatic food webs are complex, and so overzealous or short-sighted predator management within fisheries can often become detrimental in the longer term when the natural balance is perturbed. Although this general rule can break down where non-native predators interfere with ecosystems with which they have not co-evolved, predators are natural components of aquatic and other ecosystems contributing to the strength and long-term viability of fish stocks.

At only a little more than one-and-a-half millimetres in diameter and rich in yolk, the eggs of dace are nutritious and defenceless morsels preyed upon by seemingly everything that shares the water with them. Various microbes, particularly fungi, can attack eggs, many invertebrates will gladly take them, and fish from the diminutive minnow to chub and eels will raid spawn eagerly. When the alevins first hatch, they too are as vulnerable, and it is only when the dace emerge as free-swimming fry that they can evade at least some of their less mobile predators. Needless to say, the loss of eggs and alevins is huge, compensated for by the mass of eggs initially released and also by the early timing of spawning when the water is still cool enough for other life forms to be less active.

The fry swim only weakly when small, at the whim of currents unless there is adequate habitat diversity for shelter and places of respite from the strongest currents. They too are preyed upon voraciously by most species of fish, including their own kin, as well as by many types of aquatic insects. However, even when adult, dace are not the largest of fish to swim in British rivers. In fact, they are convenient 'bite-sized chunks' for various species of fish and bird, not to mention mammal.

Where dace abound, they may be the staple food of pike (*Esox lucius*), and smaller specimens are also taken by perch (*Perca fluviatilis*), chub (*Leuciscus cephalus*) and larger predatory brown trout (*Salmo trutta*) and rainbow trout (*Onchorhynchus mykiss*). Salmon (*Salmo salar*) are known to take dace; indeed, as we will relate later in this book, the dace has a special place in the history of salmon angling in the British Isles. In estuaries, bass and other predatory marine fish species may be seen harrying dace shoals.

Small dace may be taken by various predatory birds. Fry and smaller specimens may be taken by common native birds such as kingfishers (*Alcedo atthis*) and also the upland dipper (*Cinclus cinclus*). Great-crested grebes (*Podiceps cristatus*) and little grebes or dabchicks (*Podiceps ruficollis*) will also take dace fry when they occur in the calmer waters favoured by these birds. More localised on western and northern British rivers, the saw-billed ducks including goosanders (*Mergus merganser*) and the red-breasted merganser (*Mergus serrator*) are predatory ducks adapted to a fish diet, and will take smaller dace as a proportion of their diet reflective of their availability relative to other small fish species. Gulls and terns (Order *Lariformes*) too will take small dace on an opportunist basis, though they probably have no major impact on dace stocks beyond their contribution to parasite life cycles which are discussed in the following chapter.

Larger dace may be taken by grey herons (*Ardea cinerea*), another common sight on our waters, as well as the rare migrant purple heron (*Ardea purpurea*) and the nationally scarce bittern (*Botaurus stellaris*) although these latter two species generally hunt in more secluded and stiller waters than those typical of dace habitat.

The two distinct subspecies of cormorant that occur in British waters, the resident *Phalacrocorax carbo carbo* and the migratory visitor *Phalacrocorax carbo sinensis*, are well known to anglers and others who spend time by many of our lowland rivers and stillwaters. They are also well-known in terms of a polarised debate about their impacts upon dace stocks and the general wellbeing of freshwater fisheries. What is certain is that they are efficient piscivores (fish-eaters), formerly most closely associated with the coast but becoming increasingly common on inland waters as populations have boomed since the Second World War. This population growth is coincident with over-fishing of their traditional feeding grounds in coastal seas, a ban on unlicensed hunting for the bird, and also a boom in the number of inland gravel pits and other open waters, many of them overstocked with trout and coarse fish. The preferred prey of cormorants is fish of between three and sixty-five centimetres (just over an inch to twenty-six inches) long, with an ideal range between ten and thirty centimetres (four to twelve inches), of which cormorants will consume some 6-32% of their body weight each day. This equates to something like 340-520 grammes (twelve to eighteen ounces) of fish per adult bird per day. The capacity for cormorants to impact fisheries is therefore real, particularly fish in the size range of the dace, and there are equally real impacts witnessed locally on fisheries.

For some, the cormorant is a bird species to be cherished and left undisturbed. For others, booming inland cormorant numbers occur at the expense of other aspects of aquatic ecosystems, including disturbance of whole freshwater ecosystems and competitive impacts on other piscivorous birds, as well as significant economic harm. The legal status at the time of writing is equally mixed, with both strains of cormorants fully protected under both EU and UK legislation though subject to exemptions for limited culling where significant economic harm can be demonstrated (such as on vulnerable fisheries or fish farms). What is certain is that cormorants can and do take dace, and could theoretically denude waters of this 'bite-sized chunk' species if predation is intensive and sustained. Some voices in the media suggest that this is the case and occurs on a widespread basis nationally.

The other side of this argument has been raised already in the chapter addressing *Dace ecology*. Habitat impoverishment in rivers not only reduces their capacity to 'produce' dace, but also to provide refuges from predation for the fish that survive. The impacts of cormorants then have to be contextualised against the vitality of the whole river ecosystem, including pollution, abstraction, hydrology, habitat, alien species and a range of other pressures. The science has not yet been produced to assess the relative significance of cormorant predation across the British Isles though, in principle at least, we have to accept avian predators as just one of many pressures upon dace stocks, and therefore one that, all other factors being equal, an ecosystem can sustain if it is otherwise diverse, productive and healthy.

Amongst the mammals, the otter (*Lutra lutra*) will take dace and other fishes, favouring prey of between eight and twenty centimetres (three and eight inches) in length, though their favoured prey is the eel. Fish are only part of the diet, which may also include food items as diverse as bird's eggs and waterfowl. Otters have become increasingly widespread across the UK due to natural recovery once certain agricultural pesticides were banned from use. They are to be welcomed as indicators of an environment no longer too poisonous to support them, and their local impacts on formerly relatively little-predated fisheries have to be understood in that wider context. Furthermore, otters are fiercely territorial and can control substantial territories – as much as sixteen kilometres (or ten miles) of river for a dog otter and perhaps three to six kilometres (two to four miles) for a female and her kits – so their predatory pressure is spread along large expanses of river.

The rather more common and troublesome American mink (*Mustela vison*), released into the wild in the UK in the early twentieth century and still spreading rapidly, is perceived as a problem for fish stocks. However, in truth, mink are not great hunters of fish, feeding instead opportunistically on a wide range of animal species including not only fish but also waterfowl, amphibians, small mammals (they are a major factor behind the dwindling populations of the vulnerable and endangered native water vole, *Arvicola terrestris,* and water shrew*, Neomys fodiens*) and sometimes even domestic chickens and their eggs. The list of marine predators hunting dace and other fishes in estuaries may include the common seal (*Phoca vitulina*) and the grey seal (*Halichoerus grypus*).

Diseases and parasites of dace

Like all fish, dace are susceptible to a wide array of infections, parasites and other diseases. Some are specific to the species, whilst others afflict other fish species too or else are capable of exploiting damaged or vulnerable fish tissues when the opportunity presents itself. In common with most fish, it is often not a disease or parasite itself that will kill a dace, but rather its consequences for increasing the risk of predation or the entry of opportunist infections. The need for sound fishery management and careful handling of caught fish is therefore paramount.

We have already noted that dace are, like most cyprinid fish, armed with a layer of scales and these are coated with an outer layer of skin and mucus as a first line of defence to intruding organisms. The next line of defence is an immune system which operates not unlike the familiar human system, recognising foreign matter and organisms and mounting an antibody attack against them. The extent to which dace and other cyprinid fish can recover from major injury or infection is in fact quite remarkable, with older fish often showing distinctive scars or irregular patches of scales where the outer layer has healed back. Indeed, since the rigours of spawning are so intense and because water is such an effective medium for the transfer of parasites, fish generally have a truly remarkable power of recovery from injury and from some diseases.

Some general notes about parasites

Dace are subject to as wide a range of parasites – organisms that rely for all or part of their lives upon other organisms as a source of food, a safe habitat, and a place to grow and reproduce – as other cyprinid fish. Roughly 10% of all known species of plants and animals are parasitic, or else have at least one parasitic life stage. Life is tough out there in our rivers!

Many of the parasites that do the most harm are merely opportunists, exploiting the nutrient-rich bodies of fish when injury or infection opens the primary lines of defence (skin and mucus) or else weakens the immune system. It is these so-called *secondary infections* that are generally responsible for killing fish. In fact, a well-adapted parasitic organism has a vested interest in keeping the host fish healthy, as this also serves to prolong its own chances of survival and reproduction. Unless, that is, the fish is not the ultimate host organism for the parasite. In such cases, including for example various species of tapeworm or digenean flukes, the parasite can distend, blind or otherwise debilitate the host fish to maximise the chance of that fish getting eaten by a piscivorous bird, mammal or fish host in which the parasite may complete its life cycle. Scientific study has revealed that dace infected with the intermediate larvae of the digenean eyefluke *Diplostomum spathaceum* can be seriously debilitated and weakened, the parasite larvae accumulating in the eyes inhibiting visual feeding and also rendering infected dace far more vulnerable to predation by the fish-eating bird species that are the fluke's final warm-blooded hosts.

Diseases and infections occur from microorganisms living on or in dace, causing a diversity of diseases including such well-known ailments as columnaris, bacterial gill disease and bacterial fin rot, septicaemia, enteric redmouth, furunculosis, white spot, fungal attacks and various other lesser-known conditions.

Many species of larger invertebrate also have parasitic life cycles, some exploiting dace populations. Monogenean flukes generally exploit the outside of fish (the skin, gills and fins), hanging on with paired hooks. By contrast, the digenean flukes are important agents of fish disease characterised by two body suckers and no attachment hooks. They generally have multiple hosts in complex life cycles that might typically involve one or more invertebrate host organisms, a fish, and finally a warm-blooded bird or mammal. Digeneans therefore have an interest in incapacitating the fish host so that the final, generally warm-blooded host, can catch and eat it. The tapeworms are the third major group of parasitic trematode worms, some of which parasitise dace and other freshwater fish as final hosts and others of which use them as intermediate hosts and therefore tend to inflict more harm.

The spiny-headed-worms, or acanthocephalans, have a characteristic, tube-like proboscis at the front of the body. This is embedded into the gut wall of the host fish, attaching the parasite permanently with barbed hooks. Acanthocephalans then live out their lives bathed in the intestinal contents of the fish. The primary hosts of acanthocephalans are generally freshwater shrimps (family *Gammaridae*) and insect larvae, with fish serving as final hosts when they eat the primary host.

Nematodes (threadworms or roundworms) are parasitic upon virtually all other types of organisms. Well in excess of 100 species of nematode are known to be parasitic on fish, with many more as yet undiscovered. Heavy nematode infections of gills, blood, body cavities and other parts of fish can prove fatal, though it is common for fish to carry lower levels of infection with few if any symptoms.

Leeches are familiar external parasites, widespread in all freshwater habitats and characterised by muscular, annulated bodies with a sucker at each end. The various different species of leech subsist by sucking fluids from plants, vertebrates or invertebrates, including fish. Leeches may also be vectors for other disease organisms such as the flagellate *Trypanosoma* which is a blood parasite. It is most common to find leeches such as *Piscicola* species on slow-moving fish such as pike, though roach, chub and other more active species can become heavily infected where fish become inactive in cold weather or when overcrowding occurs such as during drought periods. By contrast, no doubt owing to their more active lifestyles and the lack of opportunity for leeches creeping onto them, heavy leech burdens are rarely observed on dace.

Various species of crustacean are also parasitic. The most familiar to the non-scientific angler is the fish louse (*Argulus* species). These certainly do occur on dace, although again the parasite tends to be at low levels of infection relative to more sedentary fishes, presumably because dace are always active and usually hang in mid-water.

The only parasitic mollusc that may be significant for dace are *glochidia*, the larvae of species of freshwater mussels, which may clasp onto the gills or fins of

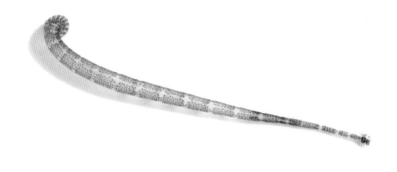

The leech Piscicola is a common opportunist parasite of various freshwater fish, though the active dace is seldom seriously afflicted.

certain fish species after hatching. Stowing away on a fish offers the larvae a degree of protection, but also helps distribute them in a river system where there is a persistent risk of getting flushed downstream and eventually out of the river. When the *glochidia* larva is ready, it releases its grip from the fish and drops to the river bed to metamorphose into an adult mussel and to assume a habit living buried in the sediment and filter-feeding fine particles from the water.

Other dace afflictions

Sometimes, dace may be found suffering from various tumours. Some of these have microbial (typically viral) causes, whilst others are more cancer-like. Some of these tumours can play an effective role in isolating infected tissues and ridding them from the body, the fish then healing to lead a perfectly normal life. Where tumours proliferate and begin to hamper the fish, dace will normally become increasingly vulnerable to predators before the tumour itself can kill the fish directly.

Faulty nutrition is rare in wild fish, other than those stunted populations where food is limited in tiny pools. However, as a fish of flowing waters, dace populations rarely seem unduly emaciated. A minor exception to this is in smaller streams where dace are not able to access richer connected feeding habitats such as on-line lakes or dams or else connections to larger rivers; in these small environments, the dace may thrive in some numbers but are rarely found growing large.

However, pollution of various sorts, often exacerbated by low flows, can result in a variety of chemical imbalances which affect dace and many other fish adversely. In particular, low dissolved oxygen levels and high concentrations of ammonia (particularly un-ionised forms of ammonia) present real threats to the health of fish. This type of impact can be exacerbated by drought, with reduced flows and associated elevated temperatures. As we have seen, dace are fish of flowing, well-oxygenated waters and have a lower thermal comfort zone than many other cyprinids that occur in the UK. If you see fish 'distressed' or 'gasping' at the surface, there is an acute problem that needs to be remedied promptly. Act immediately by contacting the appropriate regulatory agency, as they may be able to catch a polluter, stop a pollution and/or rescue the fish.

In some vulnerable parts of the country, where precipitation is acidified from often great distances away by large industrial emissions such as power stations, acidification of waters can be another stress to fish and whole ecosystems. This tends to occur predominantly in more rocky upland areas lacking in the chemicals capable of neutralising the acidity. Some parts of the upper River Wye system in mid-Wales suffer such acidification, with significant consequences for river invertebrates, salmon recruitment, stocks of other fish including dace and grayling, and the whole ecosystem that sustains them.

On some exceptional occasions, mineral deficiencies arising from unusual geology can affect fish populations, though this is very rare and is usually masked by the raft of other adverse impacts – from sheep dip chemicals to high levels of silt and nutrient inputs, or direct pollution from point sources – which blight the waters of our heavily-populated and intensively-farmed islands.

Dace may also be harmed physically, particularly as larvae, fry or small fish, by mechanical forces. Human handling can rarely be problematic though most anglers, other than hard-pressed match anglers in 'tough' venues and conditions, are unlikely to handle the smallest of dace. Fish care is, as ever, the watch-word. More significant and widespread damage can occur from the bow waves and propellers of powered boats, entrapment in weirs, hydropower schemes, pressure waves under the water from engineering works, injury arising from attacks by predators, or even the deliberate generation of shock waves as some predators stun small fish by swirling at them.

In a balanced, healthy and habitat-rich fishery, dace populations will be strong enough to resist many of these pressures. Any individual sickly fish within an otherwise healthy population is subject to Nature's impartial and efficient Darwinian game of "*survival of the most fit*", generally being seized by avian or fish predators. However, sick fish populations are always the symptom of a sick ecosystem, and it is generally imbalances in the ecosystem that stress the fish to the point where parasite infestations can run rife.

Further aspects of dace ecology

Our exploration of various aspects of dace ecology throughout Part I of this book paints a picture of a fish primarily evolved to pick drifting and floating food items from streamy water, though retreating to deeper glides at different times of the day and season where other food items are freely taken. And also, though omnivores, we have seen how the diet of dace changes with age, time of year, light levels and, consequently, the hour of the day.

Above all, dace will, like all living creatures and particularly those that are mobile within their environments, rapidly adapt their behaviour in response to environmental signals and changes that may vary from the gross to the subtle.

Dace are shoaling fish, often competing with shoal-mates for drifting food items but relying upon safety in numbers to detect and evade predators. They are also extraordinarily sensitive fish, adapted to hunting by sight but also responsive to minute chemical signals and to the most subtle of pressure waves in the dense medium of water that surrounds them.

They are cold-adapted, enabling them to exploit food resources in conditions less favoured by many other fish species. They are also able to spawn early in the year, thereby to steal a march on various would-be predators as well as competitors for food for their fry.

Streamlined and agile, suited well to shallower flowing waters not unlike habitat preferred by trout, dace can also be comfortable sharing winter quarters in steadier glides of water with other river fishes including chub, roach and perch. Dace adapt particularly well to small streams, where they may abound if conditions are suitable.

Being fish of flowing waters, and adapting readily to changing flow regimes, dace are also a fish that thrives in estuaries, and indeed in the northern Baltic Sea and other brackish waters. This exerts a physiological demand upon the dace, which need to migrate to fully fresh water to spawn, but estuarine populations can nevertheless be plentiful.

We know rather more about the migratory behaviour of dace than for many other coarse fish species, and that they are a highly mobile species that will engage in significant migrations on both daily and seasonal cycles. Any obstacle to their free movement can prejudice dace populations.

They have various natural diseases and parasites and an abundance of predators. However, human interference poses the greatest threat. Pollution, be it from large identifiable point sources or myriad industrial, agricultural and urban diffuse sources, compromises dace populations and the ecosystems of which they are a part. Water abstraction too threatens flow regimes as do impoundments such as weirs and dams, and these hydrological disruptions can change river habitats to the disadvantage of dace.

Direct habitat modification through engineering works such as unsympathetic maintenance for flood control, or indirect habitat degradation by excessive silt inputs, changes in river flow energy affecting deposition or erosion of sediment, or impoverishment of marginal habitat can also adversely affect dace viability through the impoverishment of stocks of food items or spawning and nursery habitat.

Introductions of non-native species of fishes, for example ide, or species not naturally found in a particular river, such as barbel (*Barbus barbus*), may prejudice dace by interfering with delicate ecological balances. So too, the spread of alien species of plants and animals, such as the New Zealand swamp stonecrop (*Crassula helmsii*) or American signal crayfish (*Pacifastacus leniusculus*), can perturb ecosystems through competitive, predatory, parasitic and other impacts, to the detriment of native ecosystems including their dace populations.

In his 1984 book *In Visible Waters*, John Bailey laments the cumulative impacts of these pressures on the rivers of Norfolk,

"From what I see here on the Falls stretch, the dace is a struggling species. Abstraction, spawning sites under attack from canoes or dredgers or expanding communities, frequent pollution from expanding industry, the probability of harmful agricultural chemical inflows all make the future of the dace very uncertain. Certainly, very many of this county's south-eastern rivers hold nowhere near the number of sizeable dace that they did in the 1950s or 1960s."

All of this scientific understanding of dace and the way that they live (their ecology) will serve us well not merely in appreciating the fish a little better but also in tackling aspects of angling for them by design (Part II of this book) and understanding their wider relationship with society (Part III).

Dace: The Prince of the Stream

Dace:
The Prince of the Stream

Part II. Angling for dace

Introduction to dace angling

Dace fishing? What a terrible idea!

They feed at their best, particularly the biggest spawn-laden fish, in the cold 'back end' of the season. Not only that, but the best times for fishing is when it's wet and the river is coloured up after a deluge. And then, when you've braved the elements in the coldest and darkest quarter of the year, what? Even a British record could be held in just one hand! So what's so special?

If you have bothered to read this far, you will not need telling what is so special. But let's take the trouble to say it anyhow. A small species the dace may be, the smallest of all British species that is fished for 'seriously'. Their bijou stature may devalue them in the eyes of those addicted to the cult of 'bigness' for its own sake. However, pause a moment to examine one.

Many people are fond of dace. For example, in the 1496 *Treatysse of Fysshynge With an Angle*, Dame Juliana Berners (Abbess of Shropshire) states that,

> *"The Dace is a gentyll fysshe to take."*

To this, many add an affectionate word including Arthur Bell in his 1930 *Freshwater Fishing for the Beginner* who says that,

"A jolly little fish if ever there was one."

The truth is that the dace is a marvellous species, wonderfully adapted to life in faster streams and as handsome a fish as one could ever hope to see. Fast-biting, with true specimens hard to fish for by intent, they offer sport in the most bitter of conditions when air frost dusts the trees and the dry bank-side grasses the whole short day through. As John Bailey and Roger Miller accurately observe in their 1990 book *Chub and Dace*,

> *"The dace season is a very long one. The extreme heat of high summer does not worry the fish, and in the direst of winter months we have found them to be the ones most willing to feed when temperatures plummet well below freezing point. They will feed all day long, and as dusk descends dace will feed harder still. In truth, at any time of the day, be it in bright sunlight or dull and overcast, in arctic or tropical conditions, dace will mouth a bait as long as it is presented correctly. Low, clear water does not put them down and thickly coloured floodwater will not dampen their willingness to oblige, once you find them."*

Furthermore, they may fall to the ledger, float or freeline, and to take dace on the dry or wet fly can be a joy. As Richard Franck put it eloquently in his *Northern Memoirs*, published in 1694 though written thirty and more years previously,

> *"Dace or Dare, whose darling Bait is a Gentle at the Bottom and a small Fly at the Top."*

(This is the very same Richard Franck and *Northern Memoirs* in which the oft-quoted line *"Art imitates Nature, and necessity is the mother of invention"* is written.

Like me, you may not have realised that the two clauses, each a famous quote in its own right, were part of the same classic sentence, nor that it pertains to fly fishing!)

Consequent from their willingness to feed in almost all conditions, and of the diversity of methods by which they may be taken, dace will have featured prominently amongst the first river fishing forays that many of us undertook.

Dace fishing is one of the most fun 'terrible ideas' an angler can have in British rivers!

However, there is something of a consensus of expert anglers that fishing for dace, subject to some details, falls back upon a very similar suite of methods as one needs to adopt when seeking out roach and other like 'silver fish'.

John Wilson introduces his 1992 book *Catch Roach, Rudd and Dace* by telling us why all three species are treated together in the one volume.

> *"Roach, rudd and dace are readily caught by the same techniques, on identical tackle and baits, often from the same locations, and in truth the angler is never quite sure which species will bite next...*
>
> *...scarcely is there a method, a technique or a bait that will not catch these diminutive, yet favourite species."*

The treatment of both dace and roach in one volume by 'Faddist' (Edward Ensom) in *Roach and Dace Fishing* further emphasises the similarity of methods.

Other authors emphasise the closeness of methods of dace and chub by discussing angling for them by design within the same covers. John Bailey and Roger Miller, for example, do so in their 1990 book *Chub and Dace*. Henry Bell also, in his undated text *Fly-fishing for Chub and Dace*, was another author who saw fit to treat both species in the same covers.

So, with prior guidance on fishing for dace in such agreement, and my own exhaustive coverage of all manner of approaches to catching roach within the 436 pages of *The Complete Book of the Roach* (2006), why bother to write anything more?

The answer is quite simply that this book takes the approach of exploring the biology of the fish first, and only then using that to guide thinking about ways to catch dace, bigger dace in particular, by design. What I will NOT do is replicate all of the good words on tackle and tactics that have already been written and need not be laboured again. I will assume adequate background angling knowledge or a quickness to learn on the part of the reader. After all, you will have to be a keen angler already to be reading a book on the much overlooked and sometimes maligned *Prince of the Stream*! Rather, I will focus on how to approach the fish and why, turning then to some of the special considerations that stem from this and when to deploy your already doubtlessly diverse arsenal of methods to capture them.

Fishing for dace is special. As Peter Wheat says in his 1975 book *Catch More Dace*,

> *"For as far back as I can remember dace fishing has been high on my list of angling interests... Wherever dace are found they are unceasingly popular."*

Peter Wheat further honours the hunt for big dace with the observation that the capture of bigger specimens is,

> *"...as much a challenge as any barbel, tench, carp or pike, ever was."*

The following three chapters of this book concern themselves respectively with location, bait and presentation: the three primary principles which the late and great Richard Walker elaborated as the essential stepping stones towards the capture of specimen fish by design rather than pure chance. Walker was right!

Dace, enjoyed by anglers of all ages and abilities.

However, before that, I want to finalise this introductory chapter by celebrating the unique pleasure of the catching of dace, be they big or small. As H.T. Sheringham put in his 1910 book *An Open Creel* when discussing the sheer pleasure of dace fishing on the tidal Thames,

> *"The angler might travel very much farther and fare very much worse. That is my thought every time I visit Isleworth fly-rod in hand, and it is strange if September or October does not find me there at least once in each year. I have made the expedition pretty often now, but the charm of it never fails..."*

William J. Howes, in his 1958 book *Dace: How to Catch Them*, described the dace enthusiastically as a sporting species,

> *"What the dace lacks in size is certainly made up for in gameness. If a larger fish such as a chub had the same amount of fight in proportion to size it would indeed be a difficult fish for the angler to cope with."*

And, of course, let us not forget that the pursuit of dace, as indeed of many wild coarse fish, is often an excuse for us to be out and about with a rod in our hand in some of the world's most wonderful places. As 'BB' put it in the chapter *The Fishes' Element* in his *The Fisherman's Bedside Book* (1943):

> *"One of the greatest charms of angling is that fish dwell in the pleasantest places, we subconsciously associate them with contentment and peace, with the beauty and loveliness of the earth."*

The enjoyment of catching dace is an under-represented pastime; let's see what we can do to redress the balance!

Location

What is the first step towards catching dace, and big dace in particular? Find out where they live! This is an obvious statement perhaps, but how many times do we ignore the obvious in our haste to wet a line?

We have learned a lot about the ecology of dace. At least, we have certainly learned enough to know the kinds of habitats that they prefer in different seasons and water conditions, and also the ways in which their behaviour might vary across the year and the day.

From this, it will be quite apparent that dace may not be relied upon to remain in the same place, or necessarily to be feeding when and if we find them. A moment's pause before assembling the rods or heading on auto-pilot to a favourite swim would serve us well. Everything else about catching dace is, of course, secondary to the location of fish that are either feeding or could be enticed so to do.

Where in the river will the fish be? Will this change over time, be that throughout the day or season or else in response to changing weather and river conditions, our presence and/or our bait? Remember that dace and other species of fish are like barometers, honed by nearly four billion years of evolution to respond instantly to changing river conditions.

Clues from dace biology

In his 1994 book *Freshwater Fishes of the British Isles: A Guide for Anglers and Naturalists*, Nick Giles writes the following evocative words about the ideal habitat in which dace may be found,

> *"The dace is perhaps our most graceful cyprinid species, finning in quicksilver shoals in fast-flowing crystal-clear chalkstream riffles and glides."*

This is, indeed, classic dace habitat, but it is certainly not the only place in which dace may be found. This is not just because they occur in many types of rivers other than chalk streams either. You will recall that, in the previous section of this book, we looked to the form of the dace for clues as to where these fish thrive. The body of a dace is not deep and rounded like that or a bream, rudd or carp. Neither are the paired fins, particularly the pectorals, developed into disproportionately large 'paddles' to aid the fish in fine orientation in static or slowly-flowing waters. Instead, the body of a dace is a gracefully streamlined 'torpedo', beautifully adapted to moving waters. The superficial similarity of this body shape with that of a trout, backed up by the review of swimming speeds, suggests the streamy waters to which dace are best suited.

Outside of a decent flow, the fish is at a physical disadvantage as it is not best-equipped to paddle lazily through idle waters. Nature is the ultimate economist, evolution honing species perfectly to environmental niches, which means that a dace out of place will soon be looking a predator in the face! And so it is almost without exception that dace will be found where the flows are sharp, albeit not quite the strongest of cascades wherein only trout really prosper.

Observing the biology of the fish also helps us avert some common misconceptions that can see us overlooking great dace habitat. For example, it is often written that dace are creatures of shallow streams. However, this is not automatically the case. I know of classic dace swims that are fourteen feet and more deep (or at least they were until the mill tailings fell down some time in the late 1960s). Great dace anglers like J.W. Martin (the 'Trent Otter'), Bernard Venables and William J Howes also advocated ledgering a worm tail in deep and steadier flows to locate dace when the river is pushing through strongly in winter. The form of the dace tells us instead that it is flow to which the fish is adapted, not depth.

One of the reasons commonly given for the supposed preference of the dace for shallow waters is that it is adapted for surface feeding. Again, despite the undoubted keenness of dace for taking offerings from the river's surface, the biology of the fish suggests that it is not predominantly a surface feeder.

The mouth is located at the front and suited to feeding at various depths, but is by inclination if anything slightly 'inferior' (at the front of the head yet oriented downwards) indicating an evolutionary adaptation to feeding on food suspended in the water column or on the river bed. This might inform our approach to locating feeding fish.

So, despite the oft-stated assumption that dace are fish of shallow waters, it is merely that shallow waters generally, but not exclusively, run more quickly than their deeper counterparts. But fish a rapid current at depth, like in a weir, a mill tailing or where the water scours round a corner, and there you will as likely find the dace feeding. And, of course, Mr Crabtree knew that, when the river was pushing hard in winter, roach and dace (marked by the big letters 'R' and 'D' on the surface of course!) would both be found together finding refuge in the 'easier' currents of deeper glides. Many anglers successful with big dace, myself included but also the likes of Peter Wheat and John Wilson, have noted in their written works that their best dace have often come at times when they have been roach fishing in winter in such swims. I think that John Bailey and Roger Miller put it most honestly in their 1990 book *Chub and Dace*,

> *"Of course, it could easily be said that we have just described the archetypal big roach and chub swims. That is exactly it! This is how we have caught our big dace, for as big fish I see them as having similar requirements to the other larger species that I also pursue."*

The size of dace also gives us a clue as to location. They grow to small maximum sizes as compared to river fishes such as barbel, chub and bream. Fans of small and neglected waters – and I definitely count myself in that category – know that surprisingly bulky chub and trout may await discovery in the most inauspicious-looking trickle of water, particularly those connected to bigger rivers. The same is true of dace. In fact, it is often amazing just how densely packed dace shoals can be in mill runs, channels across abandoned water meadows, floodwater cuts, tributary streams and all manner of small flowing waters associated with river systems. They can be relied upon to make good use of cover, including undercut banks, culverts, bridges, stands of in-channel vegetation be they submerged or emergent, and overhanging bushes, so much so that dense shoals of often quite big fish can be literally unsuspected under an angler's feet.

These tiny streams are criminally overlooked, but are well worth the extra effort entailed in fishing them. This is particularly so in winter where there are groundwater fed streams, the running channels of the Hampshire Avon's many abandoned water meadows being classic examples, since springs emerging fresh from underground strata produce warm water to which the dace are attracted when the main river cools. Also, as the fish run upstream to find shallow, streamy water suitable for spawning, it is easy to keep seeking them in the main rivers and overlook the minor channels in which flow conditions might be most attractive. However, whilst size offers the facility to use smaller water, it does not create an obligation so to do; dace will gladly shoal in deeper waters too when that offers them optimal current speeds, food and cover from predators.

Also, think about the predators to which dace must necessarily spend every second alert. Pike and other larger predatory fish and also piscivorous mammals can attack from anywhere. But it is predatory birds to which the dace seem most attuned. Their visibility and accessibility to aerial attack can make exposed shallows a dangerous place to be in daylight. So if there are dace in a particular stretch of river, they may be actively avoiding shallow waters during the hours of daylight or when driven there by the spawning urge, lying back in deeper water but healthy flows to intercept food items in relative safety until twilight or full darkness.

I well recall, from many years ago, my frequent walks back from the pub after closing time when I lived in Downton in south Wiltshire. The village straddles the middle Hampshire Avon and, at certain times of the year, the dace could be observed under the street lighting to be blackening the river bed of the main water meadow carrier, where by daylight there was not a single fish to be seen. John Ashley-Cooper admirably describes this dace behaviour in his 1985 book *A Ring of Wessex Water*,

"The population of dace has been patchy, but these fish behave in a curious way – here today and gone tomorrow. Looking over Ellingham Bridge in 1984 one could see on one occasion a shoal of several thousand dace. They were there for forty-eight hours, and then disappeared and were not seen again."

This migratory behaviour is well-known from scientific studies. It appears far more exaggerated where cormorants are a significant or persistent nuisance. However, Ashley-Cooper's description has more of the ring of a chance stumbling upon the dace as they were massed for spawning; the gravels below Ellingham Bridge are still a renowned spawning location for gravel-spawning species such as dace, chub and barbel.

This hyper-sensitivity to predators above the water reinforces the importance of good concealment of you, your tackle and, critically, rod or pole tips above the heads of fish which might just suddenly decide that the shallows they have been cruising in are no longer safe!

The first principle in successful angling, dictated both by the ecology of the fish itself as well as Richard Walker's incisive observations, as long ago as the 1950s when he brought the science of specimen angling to the masses, is that location is the first and most vital step towards the capture of specimen fish by design. It is my contention that thinking about the biology of the fish helps us to consider more intelligently the location of dace. Without it, we run the ever-present risk that age-old mantras and our own established habits can blind us to opportunity. As I state in my 2006 book *The Complete Book of the Roach*,

"Habit is the death-knell of successful location."

So flow then is a key, but only one of several keys. The right kind of flow has to be in proximity to a mix of habitats in which dace may shelter by day, over-winter in deeper glides, and where overhanging and marginal vegetation may add to the load of food produced by in-stream ecosystems to provide the dace with abundant drifting food items.

And, yes, dace thrive in the 'classic' shallow runs even though they may not remain there all the time! When feeding on floating matter in shallow waters, or else in the surface layers of deeper waters, they may readily be spotted feeding at the surface. As described by William J. Howes, in his 1959 *Fly-fishing for Coarse Fish*,

> *"A shoal of surface-feeding dace will disclose their whereabouts by rings on the surface. They may be in very shallow water, no more than a few inches deep, so it may be necessary to creep or crawl with extreme caution to get within casting range. Dace are quick in detecting danger, and the slightest movement of the angler may send the whole shoal dashing down the stream."*

Looking at the classic dace rivers – the Hampshire Avon, the Thames and several of its tributaries including the Kennet and the Lea and its sub-tributary the Beane, and also the Test, the Ure, the Wear, the Eden, the Thet and many more – we find reasonable flows and a diversity of habitats to support dace throughout the year. And, all too commonly, we can see the consequences of removal of these ideal conditions.

A particular casualty of human 'progress' that I explored at some length in researching this book was the Little Ouse, which rises in Norfolk and flows through into Suffolk before joining the Great Ouse River. The Little Ouse at Brandon once produced a former, long-standing British Record dace of 1lb 4oz 4dr. However, the Little Ouse today barely flows in summer, over-abstracted for agriculture and domestic use both at the surface and from the groundwater beneath.

Significant parts of its channel are constrained by unsympathetic flood defence works, it is silted by intensive land use, and the fly life is now poor. Dace do not abound in the river below the Norfolk town of Thetford. Once we get to Brandon, the river is already not much more than a lowland ditch not too dissimilar to the relatively stagnant waters of the Great Ouse where it crosses the fens many miles downstream.

Things change over time, on both long and short time scales, and we have to respond to that by using our location skills rather than relying upon habit or 'received wisdom'.

Much below 45°F (a little above 7°C), and they retreat to the kinds of steady, deep swims where one might expect to find roach and chub, with which they may mingle, and they will certainly be driven into deeper slacks and often spend a period in torpor when river temperature falls below 40°F (a little above 4°C). However, so resilient is the dace, so well adapted to cool water conditions, that it can quickly acclimate and start feeding again when the temperature is sustained for several days.

We have also to recall that dace are active, migratory fish which can not be relied upon to remain in either shallow or deep waters, or intermediate depths, for long periods of time. On a daily basis, dace are know to migrate often significant distances upstream to feed in shallower waters, and to use the width of river channels too including excursions into small tributary streams and also onto the floodplain when river levels are high.

Likewise, they are inclined to drop back into deeper waters and their associated cover at times of the year when they are most commonly found feeding in the shallows. The trick is to be adaptable to the movements and changing behaviour of the fish, and to seek to pre-empt this to some extent by learning more about their regular behaviour patterns and the ecological needs that these meet.

Sudden temperature rises in winter often send dace from deep waters into the shallows, and they are increasingly likely to do this as they get closer to spawning in the cool waters of the end of the coarse fishing closed season. As a general rule-of-thumb, bigger dace are slower to react to these mild snaps than their smaller shoal-mates, and to remain in the deeps for longer periods.

In fact, small shoals of really big dace can separate out at this time of year, perhaps since they spawn earlier than smaller fish in the same population. These shoals of larger dace may also feed in narrower dawn and dusk time 'windows' of lesser light intensity, such as those also favoured by roach.

Dace in small streams

As David Carl Forbes says in his 1966 book *Small Stream Fishing*,

> *"Dace seem to thrive in the more open type of stream, no matter
> how narrow it is, and a stream like this could produce some really
> fine dace – certainly of a better equivalent standard than roach. I
> have yet to come across a stream over-run with really small dace,
> and while there are often many to be seen, catching them is a
> very different matter. They seem to be ideally suited to the small-
> stream environment."*

I can only echo these comments and reiterate points made previously in this book
about how dace may actively search out small streams and backwaters and water
meadow channels as refuges from strong river flows, as places to over-winter or
find cover, and also to breed. Don't forget too that they are dynamic fish and, just
because they were not there when you looked, they may make extensive use of
shallow waters at some point of the day or season.

Never, ever overlook small streams, which can hold dace in appreciable numbers and sizes.

Further notes on dace location

We have also to think in three dimensions. The form of the dace is adapted to holding station in flows. Unlike the barbel, it is not flattened on the underside for a life on the river bed, nor does it have an upward-pointing mouth like the rudd or bleak which would suit it best to surface feeding. Instead, it has a graceful 'torpedo' profile enabling to exploit many depths of the river or stillwater, and exploit them dace will. We have to be prepared to locate dace at any depth in the water column as well as along a stretch of river.

As anglers, laziness is always lurking like a predatory animal around the next corner. Collectively, we devote far too small an amount of time to the location of dace, and indeed other fishes. And yet none of us would disagree that the art of catching fish starts with fishing in places that they occur! Find them, and let their location influence our thinking about the baits that might lure them and the angling methods that might deceive them, and we have found the keys to putting more or better dace on the bank!

So don't be in haste. Walk, talk and watch, spending time with those who already have a 'feel' for a stretch of river. Let its different reaches and features speak to you, as they will if you have taken time to learn a little of the biology of the dace – how they go about the tricky task of living – backed up by your own and others' accumulated experience.

Dace can also thrive in urban rivers. I well remember the pleasant surprise of a dace of a dozen ounces and a few to back it up when first I tried the River Wandle through the most urban of landscapes downstream of Wandsworth in London in the late 1970s. I was not exactly expecting a lot, as the river was constrained on both sides by unfriendly concrete and sheet piling banks and backing onto industrial estates. However, the river is, and remains today, a venue with some 'form'. I didn't know this at the time though; it was just one of the few bits of river accessible to me through a poacher-friendly hole in the wire fence to which I could cycle from my student digs! And of course another classic, accessible, free and unfailingly rewarding stretch at that time was the tidal River Thames itself at Putney, more or less facing the Fulham Football Club's 'Craven Cottage' ground across the river.

Also, sometimes just throw caution to the wind and try an unlikely-looking swim on a hunch, or spend time courting a neglected glide or side-stream. Therein may lie dace thriving on the neglect of others, fed by a rain of insects from the tangle of vegetation that makes a seemingly insignificant stream 'un-fishable', or else hanging in the lee of a snag that puts off the less adventurous angler.

This all constitutes the art, science and feeling that is 'watercraft'. Science may be your mentor and colleagues may be your tutors but, put it all together, then instinct will integrate all of that wisdom into the type of 'sixth sense' that singles out the consistently fortunate angler from his or her peers.

Bait

As we have seen by considering their feeding behaviour and food sources, dace accept a wide range of types of food (and therefore potentially bait) though their feeding behaviour may vary significantly throughout the day and across the seasons. The art of the angler is to match the bait they offer to the types of food items that dace might be already finding or anticipating, or onto which they may be coaxed to feed.

Dace hunt by sight and smell, their habitats and consequently the food they might expect to find varying throughout the seasons and time of day. It is therefore impossible to say that one particular type of bait is uniformly superior to all others. Many types of bait have their place in dace fishing. The cunning angler will think extremely carefully about what the fish require or what they may be tempted to feed upon, based on a knowledge of the ecology of the fish.

Dace in shallow, streamy waters

We know that dace prefer shallower, streamy waters in the warmer months, and also again as they approach the spawning period at the end of the coarse fishing season. We know also that they tend to migrate into these river reaches to feed at other times of the year. They do so as, like trout, they are adapted to both holding station and intercepting drifting food items in livelier currents. What dace expect in these waters are fine particles moving with the current or on its surface, though they will also graze on invertebrates on the river bed such as caddis larvae. So, by and large, this determines bait preference, not to mention presentation which we will turn to in the following chapter.

Maggots and casters are a perennial favourite of dace feeding in shallow water. They are, after all, the larvae and pupae respectively of a naturally-occurring insect, and a type of food resembling that which dace might expect to find drifting in the current in the wild.

Dace of all size absolutely love red maggots.

In my experience, red maggots out-fish other types of maggot, a point upon which William J. Howes agrees in his 1958 book *Dace: How to Catch Them*. However, Howes also states that dace sometimes prefer other specific colours including green-tinged maggots, a preference for which he attributes to the high vegetable content of the diet of a dace. Howes also suggests that bunches of maggots are a poor hook bait as this encourages dace to nip the ends of the larvae. This does not tally with my experience, though it is easier to present single or double maggots on the hook in the most natural manner. In any event, maggots presented with the flow amongst small handfuls or catapult pouches full of free offerings can encourage the dace to feed freely. This is particularly the case where many fish are present and they begin to compete to reach drifting food items first. Beware, however, of feeding too heavily. This may fill the fish up, attract unwanted species such as chub, or cause the dace to follow excess sinking bait downstream or onto the bed of the river. It can also drive any minnows and bleak present into a feeding frenzy, which can be a complete pain! In slightly deeper water, such light feeding can raise dace up in the water column to intercept falling baits. Another little tip here

Casters are another first-class bait for dace.

is that, when the dace are in a frenzy, a little red wool on the hook offered amongst free offerings of red maggots, or small red worms, can be highly effective and save time in re-baiting. Now that rubber maggots in various colours and buoyancies are readily available from tackle shops, I recommend them too.

Casters too can be offered in exactly the same ways, free-lined or under a waggler or stick float, once the dace have been 'warmed up' by small handfuls of free offerings thrown or catapulted into the swim at regular intervals. Casters are wonderfully attractive baits on their day, and have the advantage in shallow waters of often being a little more buoyant than maggots.

Hemp is another bait that can be offered effectively for dace in shallow waters in the manner described for maggots. Dace certainly home in on the black grains, even when they fall to the river bed. I have seen them pick over a bed of mixed wheat and hemp on a stream bed leaving only the wheat grains in their wake. You can buy pre-cooked or tinned hemp from tackle shops, but I find that freshly-boiled hemp is best.

The preferred method for preparing hemp is to bring some to the boil in a pan of water to which has been added a little bicarbonate of soda to blacken the husk and some sugar to offset the bitterness of the bicarb. Alternatively, fill a thermos flask one-third full with hemp, and no more as when the grains expand they might otherwise burst the flask, then top up with boiling water and let that stew overnight or during a working day. In either case, don't waste the liquor in which the hemp is prepared as this is an attractant that may be added to ground bait. You can also freeze unused cooked hemp grains for later use, although fresher grains are best for hook-bait as they are more durable.

There are various methods for attaching hemp to the hook which include pushing the hook bend into the cracked edge of the grain, bonding with a spot of superglue, inserting the point into the site of stalk attachment at the top of the grain, or else using artificial hemp on the hook. When exciting a shoal of dace with free offerings of hemp, a lightly boiled tare – a sort of small dark pea commonly used to feed caged birds – presented on the hook can be deadly as the fish compete for these larger grains. Likewise, hemp and casters, the latter on the hook and the former as free offerings, is a highly effective combination on its day for dace feeding in open waters. With hemp and other fine particle baits, you can expect very quick bites which need to be hit rapidly but gently.

Other effective particle baits that can be offered thus in streamy water include sweetcorn, sunflower kernels, elderberries, baked beans (floated first in a little water to dissolve away the tomato sauce), scraps of pasta and many other types of seed sold to feed pet birds.

Also, let us not forget wheat, an old traditional bait and a personal favourite of mine. Wheat too needs to be simmered for perhaps twenty minutes before being left to swell, and it is effective for all manner of fish species in either natural or else coloured and/or flavoured forms. Boiled wheat, also known as stewed or creed wheat, is essentially a natural bait, being the seed of a species of grass like many others that enter watercourses in great numbers and which feeding dace will intercept on the drift. You must cook it well though, as too many uncooked grains may otherwise take on water inside the fish and swell with potentially damaging consequences. You can, if you so choose, get more elaborate in its preparation. For example, in *The Compleat Angler*, Izaak Walton suggests,

> *"You may make another choice bait thus: take a handful or two of the best and biggest wheat you can get; boil it in a little milk, like as frumity is boiled; boil it so till it be soft; and then fry it, very leisurely, with honey, and a little beaten saffron dissolved in milk; and you will find this a choice bait, and good, I think, for any fish, especially for Roach, Dace, Chub, or Grayling..."*

Another little trick of mine which is really effective for dace, as indeed for roach and chub, is finely-diced luncheon meat. Improbable as it sounds, it is highly effective. I stumbled upon this technique after catching many dace, including some surprisingly small ones, on great big lumps of 'meat' legered or trotted for barbel or chub over a number of years. The next experiment was therefore to put finely-diced luncheon meat cubes on the hook and offer this on stick float or waggler tactics with several chunks of free offerings. Hey Presto! A deadly method was discovered and I share this secret with you now. Bread punches, or the meat punches that one can now buy, also serve to produce consistent hookable discs cut from sheets of luncheon meat. We should not be surprised about this carnivorous streak, as dace have a marked preference for meaty baits. Some people I know have found minced steak offered in a similar way to be very effective for them.

Red worms and brandlings too are highly effective baits for presenting to dace in shallow waters. They are, however, just the tip of the proverbial iceberg when it comes to using natural baits which may be found in the river or on its banks. After all, drift-feeding fish are sure to be tuned in to any potential food item that enters the water. My best advice here is to carry a small, fine-meshed hand net with you during the summer months, and to try offering dace anything you catch on the bank top or under vegetation or stones in the river channel. Caddis larvae, the familiar cased insects that are the larval form of sedge flies, are a traditional favourite when removed from their cases. They are much loved by dace and recommended by everyone from Izaac Walton to William J. Howes. Small water snails feature prominently in the diets of dace, though I have not had a lot of success with them as a hook bait for either dace or roach. Freshwater shrimps, however, are eagerly seized by dace, as are small dried (marine) shrimps procured from oriental supermarkets. So too are hog-lice, also known as water slaters, though similar-looking terrestrial woodlice appear to actively repel fish. Do not discount using any small fish that you catch in your net! Dace are opportunists, and will take a dead or live fish small enough to swallow.

Bloodworms and jokers are another 'natural' bait, though they have little or no place in specimen dace-fishing circumstances. However, for the match angler, they may give an edge to reluctant dace in cold conditions, though fishing flowing waters this way can get expensive.

Another traditional bait is trotted 'silkweed', which can be gathered from hard surfaces underwater, hooked then trotted to feeding fish. Dace will take it, and I have done well on it in years gone by, though it is not a method I often use today. This is for the simple reason that modern rivers are massively enriched with chemical nutrients compared to yesteryear, with the resultant growth of abundant masses of filamentous algae including many algal species which are more wiry and less palatable to dace and other coarse fish. The fish are today so surrounded by filamentous algae in their 'natural' environments that a little more on a hook is like baiting with a single leaf in a rainforest!

Bread is a bait that is both supremely versatile and a major attractor of dace, particularly big dace, in virtually all conditions. Offered on freeline (often dipped first in water to aid longer casting) or under float or by ledger, bread can be adapted to most feeding conditions including streamy waters. It may be white or brown, offered as flake, paste, punched bread, crust or uncooked dough, either natural or else coloured and/or flavoured.

My personal preference is almost exclusively for natural white breadflake, from the cheapest white loaves available, which bigger dace really go for. However, other authorities offer some interesting permutations. Two from William J. Howes, in his 1958 book *Dace: How to Catch Them*, are worthy of comment,

> *"It is essential that bread paste is made sufficiently stiff to remain on the hook… when fished in the swift, streamy waters so typical of dace swims. A very softy paste, though it may be preferred by dace, means frequently baiting the hook."*

> *"As a variation of the familiar cubes, the crust may be cut into triangular pieces… The attraction lies mainly in its movements, especially in fast water, for its antics certainly attract the attentions of dace."*

Of the former – hard paste – I disagree diametrically! Soft paste, only just thick enough to stay on during the cast, is essential firstly for an unimpeded hook point on the strike and also to prevent hard lumps of paste being retrieved repeatedly through a shoal of dace. This makes them suspicious of the bait and generally nervous.

Of the latter 'tip' about triangular crust, this might work for small dace, but a natural presentation is essential for large dace intercepting drift from the flow. However, both of Howes' suggestions demonstrate a thinking and innovating angler which, though I might disagree on some details, is an approach that I wholeheartedly endorse!

Loose feed to entice dace to feed on bread need not be complex or expensive. Slices of bread, ideally stale but certainly not musty, can be mashed in water to produce 'slops' which break up in the flow exciting the dace. To produce a 'cloud' bait – one that will break up into a fine mist in the water – start with completely air- or oven-dried bread or else mash up a few wetted 'Rich Tea' biscuits with the bread. For all such 'slops', you will need to vary the consistency, whether by the amount of water initially added or the quantity of dried crumb added subsequently to stiffen it up. Use harder groundbait for deeper swims and a looser mix that breaks up more quickly in shallower waters or the surface layers of deeper water.

My preferred method for free offerings of bread is to liquidise some fresh slices. The resultant moist crumb is readily compacted in the hand for throwing, but breaks up into a fine mist on contact with water. In deeper waters, you may squeeze it harder to delay the break-up, and can even wrap it around a pebble from the river bank, or else add gravel to the bait tub, to get it to sink more quickly. Liquidised bread can also be packed into swimfeeders, from which it will be released as a fine mist as the bread takes on water when cast into the river.

I pass on a tip from David Carl Forbes' 1966 book *Small Stream Fishing*, which I have never tried! However, so bizarre does fishing with mildewed bread sound, and so likely to succeed for those with stronger stomachs as it entails natural foods, that I will be trying it!

"Bread stored in a damp space will soon become covered in mildew, but do not let it deter you if you find yourself left with nothing but mildewed bread. It may not be hygienic, but it mixes up into an attractive bait which I consider to be unbeatable. The finished product is dark green in colour and extremely strong-smelling, and I do not know whether it is the colour or the natural vegetable smell which makes this mixture so attractive."

Many more types of bait can work with dramatic effect for dace in shallow waters. One particularly interesting option is discussed by William J. Howes in his 1958 *Dace: How to Catch Them*, when discussing fishing for dace attracted to raked swims,

"The old Thames professionals often did this, and baiting with a tiny piece of red cloth they have been known to take as many as 300 dace in a day."

This is obviously similar to my red wool trick, elaborated earlier. It works once the dace are feeding freely and, ideally, competing for food items with less effort spent on close inspection.

Choice of bait will depend upon many circumstances, including obviously what you have with you or can find on the bank, but also what the fish appear to be eating and which other species are in the swim with them. For example, if the river is alive with bleak or minnows you might want to avoid baits like maggots unless you are confident of 'feeding them off'. In this circumstances, the larger grains of sweetcorn can be a winner.

Do synthetic baits like mini-boilies and pellets have a role in dace fishing? I personally have not found one, though I am sure others may have done so. We can expect them to work in some circumstances as, after all, each is made from natural ingredients such as eggs, milk protein, fish meal, etc. which dace should recognise and accept. But, with such an abundance of cheaper and more readily-available alternatives, I have never found the need to go for anything more high-tech, particularly so when offering baits to fish attuned to intercepting drift in shallow waters and doing so predominantly by sight.

I should also at this point mention again the emergence of artificial baits: plastic sweetcorn, maggots of all colours, synthetic bread and pellets, etc. Some folks swear by 'artificials' as a hook bait; I more often find myself swearing at them! Do experiment if you feel so moved, and good luck with them, but in my direct experience offering a 'real' bait amongst 'real' free offerings is, with the exception of artificial hemp, likely to get the best results.

The list of potential baits is almost endless, including cheese in all its forms, pastry, greaves, pearly barley, raisins and many more, all of which may have their day. However, you have got the basic principles here and can innovate on your own. I do so myself a lot of the time (see my comments about luncheon meat which came from experimentation). Please share any of your notable successes with me!

I have left until almost last natural or artificial flies on the surface or fished beneath it. Dace are well-known for rising to take floating insects, and so a dapped or fly-fished offering can be really effective when the fish are shoaled in shallow water or dimpling the surface in deeper runs.

And finally, I'll just mention small lures, which we will discuss in the next chapter. Don't forget the often-overlooked predatory instincts of these little fish!

Dace in deeper glides

As we have observed, there are times of year, particularly during the cooler months, when dace positively prefer deeper waters where currents are present but are not excessively strong. However, currents there will be, for dace are generally not fish of slack water to which their streamlined and elongated bodies are not ideally adapted. At this time of year, we might tackle dace in other ways and using some of the same baits but also some quite different ones.

As many readers will recall from their copies of Bernard Venables' classic book *Mr Crabtree Goes Fishing*, Mr Crabtree favoured using a legered lobworm tail in an eddy when the river was in spate in winter. Dace will also follow an advancing front of flood water across fields, and I have done very well catching dace and roach from waterside car parks beside the Hampshire Avon when the river has spilled out onto them. William J. Howes, in his 1958 book *Dace: How to Catch Them*, also recommends big loworms for big dace. In fact, Howes is an advocate of mounting lobworms on a Pennell rig (a two-hooked terminal rig with one hook embedded in each end of the worm) though this is probably unnecessary. J W Martin too, the 'Trent Otter', advocated angling for dace with big lobworms on deep swims on the River Trent in his *My Fishing Days and Fishing Ways*. I too have had some notable (albeit accidental) successes with large dace from the rivers Wye and Hampshire Avon under spate conditions when tracking down barbel with big lobworms.

It remains quite true that dace will seek slacker water in strong flows, and they will also often do so in chillier water in the depths of winter when they need to expend less of their energy fighting currents. Offering a piece of meaty worm in these conditions remains an effective method for taking many species of fish, including bigger dace which are in no way shy of big baits nor heavier tackle. You might also try little bits of luncheon meat too, as elaborated earlier in this chapter.

It is my experience and that of many other specimen dace anglers that bread really comes into its own in deeper glides. Big lumps of flake or paste offered by ledger or float, supported by adequately stiff mixtures of feed to cut down through the water as balls or in swimfeeders before breaking up, can certainly sort out the heftier dace as they lay over-wintering. Where smaller dace are present, punched bread, on both the float and ledger may outscore flake.

Dace in estuaries

Estuaries seem to suit dace very well. I have had many happy hours chasing them with ledger, float and fly tactics in the lower tidal reaches of both the Dorset

Stour and the Hampshire Avon, including their meeting place at Christchurch Harbour. Also, the tidal Thames is an excellent dace river which has thrown up for me some surprisingly big fish, as have the tidal lower reaches of the River Exe and other rivers besides. For a fish so versatile in stronger flows, the unpredictable and changeable currents of estuaries present no great challenge, other than the profusion of both marine and freshwater predators that can harass the dace shoals that frequently abound there.

Excess finesse is a positive handicap in these dynamic flowing-water systems. Leads and feeders adequate to hold bottom, heavy floats and bulk weights to trot through at the right feeding depth, and wagglers of decent size to fire out and control at some distance when feeding shoals show near the surface in mid-river all have a place. The location and habits of dace can also switch by the instant as tide and current change; sometimes the dace will follow a current and vacate your reach of river entirely, leaving it to chub, roach, bream, flounders, mullet or who knows what! Estuaries are exciting places, and need to be tackled with hefty enough tackle if they are not to daunt you.

Groundbait should be suited to conditions. You will also need decent-sized catapults to fire out maggots or casters if the dace are feeding in the surface layer, or balls of groundbait sometimes mixed with gravel or moulded around stones when the fish are feeding deep down. Alternating between swimfeeder and loafer or Avon float tactics can be useful when the fish are on the river bed, the feeder getting the bait directly to them and the float following it in the flow.

I recall one excellent tidal cycle that I fished with a friend on the tidal Exe. Steve is an excellent match angler who persisted for an hour until contacting dace near the surface with 'wag and mag' tactics. He then caught a lot of dace and some quite nice specimens too. Meanwhile, I had started with the waggler in the surface layer, progressively deepening my rig in an attempt to find the fish until I found the river bed. Then, a heavy Avon float fed from a centrepin offered best presentation, and a switch of bait to chunks of flake with liquidised bread found the fish in receptive mood as I started to hit the chub and roach with occasional dace. When sport slowed as the current strengthened, I moved to the swimfeeder and quivertip rig, the feeder packed with crumb and some flake on the hook which dace hit with some force in the fast ebb. As the water shallowed with the falling tide, the dace grew less confident with a static bait, bites not slowing down at all but fewer fish connecting on the strike. This signalled a need to change bait and tactics, so it was back to maggots and waggler to coax the evidently dense shoal up in the shallowing water column. The last half-hour or so of the session was a frenzy of dace activity in the fast, shallow water, with the fish gradually drawn right under the rod tip.

This story is instructive in at least a couple of ways. Firstly, and the point of its inclusion in this chapter, is that changing bait and the way it is offered can maximise success over a short period of time. Secondly, changing presentation (the topic of the next chapter) in response to changing river conditions will keep you catching when reliance on just one method may not.

Dace in stiller water

Perhaps I fish in the wrong places, but I have never found that dace tend to hang where currents are slight. Nature has not adapted them so to do. In the following chapter dealing with presentation, we will look briefly at methods for presenting static baits in such conditions. William J. Howes notes in his book *Dace: How to Catch Them* that 'live' baits such as worms of maggots are better in these relatively static conditions as their movement adds attraction.

More thoughts about dace baits

Even if you stumble upon a killing bait, remember that river conditions and the behaviour of fish change constantly with the hour of the day and the turn of the season. Each bait has its moment, which may be brief albeit intense. The key factor to bear in mind is that the ecology of the fish provides us with the clues we need to select the best bait for the moment, not habits informed by what worked well once! Keep thinking like the fish and keep innovating accordingly.

Whatever bait you use, don't forget how phenomenally sensitive dace are to chemicals. All baits therefore have to be in tip-top conditions, avoiding all taints of petrol, nicotine, urine, synthetic soaps or other chemicals, after-shave, sweaty maggots, musty bread, etc. Good quality, fresh and untainted bait will never let you down if selected and used wisely.

Dace as bait

The final word in this bait chapter has to go to the use of dace as bait. For many pike anglers, dace are perceived as a perfect pike bait – fished dead or alive and mounted either on hooks or spinning flights – due to their size, silvery appearance and toughness. In his 1942 book *Coarse Fish*, E. Marshall Hardy writes that,

> *"For me the principal usefulness of Dace is as bait for Pike..."*

He is not alone in this opinion. The Reverend W. Houghton, in his 1879 book *British Fresh-Water Fishes*, also notes that,

> *"The Dace, from its brilliant appearance, is an excellent bait in trolling for Pike, especially when the water is discoloured."*

I have certainly caught my share of big pike on dead dace fished in a mobile way, sink-and-draw beneath a sliding float on strongly-flowing rivers, the pike hitting the baits very hard as they 'swim' above their heads. However, at this point I will leave the topic of pike angling which belongs in another book.

Dace and the British Record salmon

In concluding, it is worth recalling the role of dace in the downfall of one of the most famous of British Record fish. All chapters are, after all, best ended with a tale of drama and curiosity!

The fish in question is none other than the phenomenal sixty-four pound Atlantic salmon taken by Miss Georgina W. Ballantine of Glendelvine whilst fishing the River Tay way back on Saturday 7th October 1922. Though the various published accounts of the fish vary in some details, it seems to have measured a staggering four-and-a-half feet long (that's over one-and-one-third metres in 'new money') with a girth of some twenty-eight-and-a-half inches (over seventy-two centimetres).

Miss Ballantine was born, lived and died in a cottage just a good cast away from the Boat Pool. Her father was the registrar of the area and a friend of Sir Alexander Lyle, of the Glendelvine estate. (Some other accounts have it that her father was the gillie on the Murthly beat). Father and daughter were standing in for the laird, who was unable to fish on that fateful day. The father was in charge of the oars of the boat from which Miss Ballantine began spinning in the late afternoon in the Boat Pool above Caputh Bridge on the Murthly beat.

The bait in question was a dace. Again, there are varying accounts of exactly what this 'dace' really was. Some record that it was a two-inch dace deadbait which her father had mounted in a Malloch's spinning mount, trailed from the boat. It would in all probability have been a preserved fish were that the case; dace were then absent from Scotland. However, in an article in Volume 50 of the magazine *Waterlog*, Derek Mills records that the Tweed was found to hold a thriving dace population in the 1960s and 1970s and that this seems likely to have resulted from salmon anglers releasing baits brought to the river to use in spinning mounts when salmon fishing. Perhaps then a freshly-killed dace, imported live for this purpose, was on Miss Ballantine's flight? Most likely, we will never know. Other accounts refer to a 'lacquered dace', though whether this was a real lacquered fish or a man-made lacquered lure also remains veiled in mystery. Other sources record a 'spinning dace' or a 'spinning dace minnow bait', which again may have been a lure or a dead fish.

Whatever the exact identify of the dace, we do know that the mighty salmon grabbed the bait at around 6:15 pm as it was getting dark and the pair were preparing to return to shore and leave the river. The fish initially moved slowly downriver, the pair beaching the boat for Miss Ballantine to fight the mighty salmon from the bank. However, they quickly took to the boat once again as 'the Beast' (as Miss Ballantine had come to call it) made a run down the river and through the near-side support of Murthly Bridge, out of the Boat Pool. After a dogged fight of two hours and five minutes, the fish was eventually landed at 8:20 pm over a half-mile down the river.

And, though the precise nature of the dace bait is less than certain, the rest at least is history!

Presenting bait to dace

The third of Walker's three key steps towards the capture of big fish by design is *presentation*. Having first found the fish (*location*) and then successfully determined what food they will accept (*bait*), the task then is to offer them something tasty on our hooks by means that both offer it in a suitably natural fashion but which also enable you to detect when the fish takes the bait. Control is a key consideration here: you have to remain in control of your bait at all times or else it will as likely behave in an unnatural manner, either dissuading or positively scaring off the fish you are targeting. Understandably, there are many means for achieving this.

Presentation, technique and tackle

To read much of the modern angling press and the plethora of angling tackle catalogues, you could be forgiven for thinking that the priority was to buy the 'best' and most modern kit to achieve this. However, tackle remains, in my opinion, the very last consideration in a chain that leads from (1) reaching the fish in their feeding location with (2) a bait that they will accept, (3) this presented in as subtle and natural a manner as possible using appropriate (4) techniques. Oh yes, and (5) the right tackle to get the job done!

So am I saying that tackle is not important? No, not a bit of it! What I am suggesting, however, is that the choice of tackle is the last consideration once the method of attack has been finely thought through from the starting point of the biology of the fish. Reaching for the pole for pinpoint presentation to visible fish in a shallow run may seem logical from the 'tackle-first' point of view, but think from the perspective of the fish and its heightened sense – in fact almost total paranoia – about aerial attack in these vulnerable waters and then you will realise that the overhead movement of a pole will be the kiss of death upon dace fishing in that swim. Likewise, breaking out the stick float in a deep and turbulent run may give you the impression of finesse of presentation, but the current will probably be dragging the bait hither and thither in a wholly unnatural way and probably not even letting it reach the deeper feeding depths where the dace may lie. The right tackle is of crucial importance, but only when the unique circumstances have been appraised. To catch large dace consistently, you need to master as broad a range of techniques as are appropriate to the waters in which they swim.

So how have these inverted, albeit largely subliminal, messages about the supremacy of tackle over technique come to dominate the angling press? The answer is money! When I was a lad (I swore I'd never resort to saying that when I was younger!) in the 1960s and early 1970s, I had just missed the publication of the famous *Creel* magazine, though I knew of it by repute. No, mine was the era of *Mr Crabtree Goes Fishing* and of the delightful *Angling* magazine. Now, *Angling* was a fantastic monthly read, and a worthy successor to *Creel*. It devoted its pages variously to stalking mullet in harbours, trotting for chub and roach on swift chalk rivers, the pursuit of halibut on the high seas, dry fly fishing for wily brown trout in crystal flows, chumming for Cornish mako sharks, and a million other topics besides, including my favourite series of all titled *Fighting Talk* which dealt with all aspects of playing fish. Specialist carp fishing was in its infancy, or perhaps its junior school years, with guarded talk of 'HNVs' (high nutrient value baits) and all such arcane innovations. You could buy Avon rods and stepped-up carp rods. However, for most anglers, including many aspiring specimen-hunters, regular twelve-foot glass fibre rods paired with either Mitchell or Intrepid reels served every purpose from trotting out roach to offering floating crust for carp, lure fishing for pike and all points between.

What a difference a decade makes! I went to university in London in the middle-1970s, reluctantly leaving behind the musty odours of linseed oil and varnish which then characterised tackle shops. I fished periodically, mainly with whatever tackle I already had and using bread scraps for bait, but in truth my time was largely dictated by the demands of undergraduate and then postgraduate studies, not to mention a heavy allocation of my limited resources to hormones, bonhomie, beer and a fledgling first career as a rock guitarist with all that that entailed. To cut a long and hazy story very much shorter, I really didn't step in earnest into a tackle shop until the early-to-middle 1980s, and I found myself in an alien world. The instant impression was the wholesale displacement of yesterday's odours of musty preservatives with all manner of synthetic chemical pongs! Wooden rods were things of yesteryear and knotted string nets were relegated to the annals of history along with porcupine quill floats and, oddly, anything that was not made of black plastic, be that carbon fibre, extruded plastic floats or luggage. Yesterday's 'local brands' – Sealey, Grice and Young, K.P. Morritt, Strikeright, Milbro, the East Anglian Rod Company, and all manner of others – were no more, swept aside by phalanxes of shiny products manufactured by the multinational corporations, many of them Japanese, which were now multi-billion dollar global conglomerates. Instead of rods and reels being known by local names reflecting the region or locality of their design or application – 'Sheffield', 'Nottingham', Leeds', 'Avon' and so forth – corporate 'branding' took over as ubiquitously as it had in the fashion and music industries, with the beginnings of the plague of 'celebrity endorsements'! Bite indicators no longer swung or lifted but instead bleeped and flashed, and every store carried a range of camping accessories to assist – horror of horrors – an angler to sleep more comfortably when fishing! To say that I was in culture shock on my re-engagement with the sport was an understatement.

Much else had changed too. The long-serving British Records of yesterday were largely brushed aside by hitherto unimaginable fish, or at least for those species such as tench, carp, bream and others for which a static approach was aided by modern self-hooking methods and baits. It was nice to see that the familiar records for dace and rudd still remained as, along with that for roach which had changed little, the tectonic shift in tackle technology had not skewed the playing field so radically for those mobile species for which an equally mobile approach paid dividends. For them, there were slighter rewards to be won from prolonged sessions with instant-hooking rigs, fishing for specimens grown large on wheelbarrows full of synthetic baits and doubtless abetted by the local effects of climate change and the general enrichment of waters with nutrient chemicals from agriculture and sewage effluent. Perhaps, in those large stillwaters and bigger rivers, novel tackle, bait and approaches were helping us catch fish that were always there. However, the age-old arts of trotting or ledgering simple baits in an ever-changing river were yet to be bettered when it came to luring smaller, native silver species.

The face of angling publications had also changed massively, as I found to my surprise when I started once again to contribute articles on resuming my specimen interests. Gone was *Angling* magazine, and gone were virtually all other publications which aspired to write of the simple virtues, the exotic pleasures that the common man like me might never savour other than vicariously in print, and the great diversity that is our sport. Gone was extensive coverage of sea angling and fly fishing in the weekly magazines. Gone too much of the romantic writing that eulogised the great rivers and pools, the characters on the river bank, and the bucolic grandeur of just being there by the water with rod in hand.

As I got to know the new breed of magazine editors, mainly 'businessmen' first rather than nutty old anglers with a side-interest in the printed word, the magnitude of the revolution in my near-decade of angling abstinence was brought home to me. The 'mixed species' publications had died, so I was told, at the hands of the multinational companies that had come to dominate the tackle market. Magazines survived by selling advertising, and the big companies wanted focused magazines to concentrate the pool of 'punters' potentially interested in their brands.

This was, let's recall, the decade of 'Thatcherism' and 'Reaganomics', which collectively changed the world order to posit profit as the overriding principle in everything from industry, international competition, health care and dace angling. This was the decade when societal concern for public health and wellbeing was usurped by the absurd idea that the generation of profit would enable us to buy anything that we, or at least those who controlled the purse-strings, so decided. Everything had a price tag, and the old order of 'value for its own sake' was overturned, perhaps forever. This was the age when publishing houses changed from interest-driven to profit-driven ventures, fuelled and steered to an ever-declining extent by direct sales and more by the largesse of advertising revenues. Though no angling editor of that era ever said it to me quite so directly, the sense that was most strongly conveyed was that he who paid the piper most certainly dictated the goddamned tune that he played!

So just one of the unsung victims of the 'greed is good' decade was the 'multi species' angling publication, which gave space to smaller fish and other minority interests, as advertisers drove the subdivision into increasing specialties. The age of the generalist angler began to pass, as the market for tackle and the publications that promoted it became characterised by targeted advertising, interspersed with a few articles and photographs! And those articles have since become ever-more technique-based, a tacit marketing ploy for tackle, rather than celebrating the simple pleasure of fishing and, heaven forbid, not even caring if you caught anything! This is, of course, a deliberately grotesque picture. However, there are certainly significant elements of it that many older 'angling pros' will endorse, be that in public or in private.

And so, as global macroeconomic policies progressively capitalised very facet of modern life, angling too changed fundamentally. Except for some quiet backwaters that is. Those who enjoy stalking a small stream to offer free-lined bread to dace may just, like me, still be using rods and reels from the 1960s and 70s and fishing in waters small enough not to be seen as major economic assets by land-owners, some of whom are still happy enough to allow you to dabble in them for the 'price' of a bottle of whisky a year.

And so, my rant about the globalisation of the tackle industry and commercialisation of fishing over, let's get back to the issue of suitable tackle for dace fishing!

Is modern tackle then inferior to its 'classic' counterparts from days gone by? Not a bit of it! When trotting a big river, give me a light, durable and long float rod any day of the week. I am with Richard Walker in putting aside more fragile and substantially heavier wooden rods as soon as I was able! Likewise, modern fine-wired and chemically-sharpened hooks of consistently high quality are a huge advance in offering baits in an unimpeded manner, hooking fish effectively, and minimising harm to them on unhooking. Contemporary fluorocarbon and braid lines can, in appropriate circumstances, offer advantages over nylon monofilament which itself is manufactured today far finer and of a more consistent quality than ever before. And also I can now buy a reel for under £4 which is technically superior in every department to the first really high-quality reel I bought in the early 1970s for twice that sum! The cost element arising from globalised industry also brings tackle within the reach of everyone, albeit that you can still expect to spend 'top dollar' for the very best.

So, has modern tackle completely usurped its forebears and older materials? Again, not a bit of it! I still regularly use glass fibre rods from the 1960s and 70s, and several different centrepin reels from that era and before. Some of my mates love the 'alive' feel of a split cane rod, built today by craftsmen blessed with better equipment and an unprecedented consistency of raw materials to produce something that is simultaneously a highly effective angling tool and a living work of art. For me, you can happily relegate to the history books the old, heavy fish-harming hooks and the inconsistent, kinking nylon lines that I grew up with. Also, I note, the idea of using gut or horsehair lines does not seem attractive to 'vintage' angling aficionados! I like some of the old fixed spool reels, but this is mainly dewy-eyes nostalgia and the re-living of old memories; I don't actually use the damned things as not only are mine all pretty battle-scarred but they are just not as good as the lighter, freely-running, weatherproof models I have replaced them with.

In the balance of old and new tackle, there are polar opposites among us. Tackle companies and those writers, editors and users seduced by them will always argue that it is essential to be nearest the 'cutting edge' to give yourself the greatest advantage. The vintage tackle 'nut' will argue the converse although, as I have said above, none that I fish with think seriously of going back to gut, horsehair and crudely hewn, thick-wired hooks with inconsistently ground points. Added to which, 'tradition' is such a mutable concept. When was this Golden Age to which 'tradition' relates?

The term 'vintage' is generally applied (in wider circles and not angling) as relating to things of 25 years old and more, but few would argue that the 1980s was such a Golden Age, whether for music, taste, global ethics or fishing tackle! So are we talking of the 1970s, 60s, 50s, 20s, Walton's day during the English Civil War, the Dark Ages, or the Stone Age when people across the globe angled with hooks hewn from animal bone? You could go mad creating a cogent argument as to which arbitrary point in time best represented 'traditional' angling. You will have to address the facts that today's fishing methods are just tomorrow's new 'tradition' (to which an old Diana Ross song more or less alluded!) Does it matter at all what we call 'traditional angling methods' if it makes us feel good? (Diana Ross may have sung a song about that too for all I know!)

However, what we can probably agree upon is, irrespective of the tools we pick up to achieve that end, there are traditional values of enjoyment of the waterside and the life that occurs there, respect for nature, watercraft, good company, and pitting our primeval wits against the generally superior wits of the fish we hunt! To each their own, I say. The only two criteria of any importance are: (1) does your choice of tackle enable you to present your bait effectively; and (2) is it fun? I like using old centrepin reels on modern rods for trotting, using modern lines, extruded plastic floats and chemically-sharpened hooks. Are the masonry nails that I use as bulk weights (and which are discussed later) 'traditional'? Discuss!

The 'take-home' message is quite simply that tackle should be your servant, not your master, supporting you in your chosen technique to present appropriate bait to the fish where they are feeding. End of message!

For this reason, I will not devote a whole chapter on the tackle itself (if you want to see an exhaustive treatise on appropriate methods and tools then I suggest you consult my 2006 *The Complete Book of the Roach*). Rather, I will mention appropriate 'tools of the trade' when addressing methods best suited for presenting bait to dace in different circumstances.

Time spent not dace fishing

Whether for location, bait selection or determining methods of presentation, time by the water spent NOT dace fishing can be the most productive angling time of all. It is all too easy to let your enthusiasm to wet a line take over, and to assume also that the more hours the line is wet, the greater your chances.

However, it is in reality better to think things through and thereby bypass habits of fishery, swim, bait and tackle selection. As Richard Walker put it (and many other things beside) so succinctly,

"Mental laziness is fatal in all kinds of fishing."

More poetically, but with equal wisdom, W E Davies states in *The Technique of Freshwater Fishing and Tackle Tinkering* that,

"'Make haste slowly' must have originated on a stream. Fishing is the time to philosophize. Use your head. Good tackle is an asset, naturally, but a little brain work will help it from becoming 'rusty'."

The message is as simple as it is consistent. Think first!

Concealment

One of the most important elements of dace location is that they do not locate you before you locate them! It may sound obvious, but the importance of this can not be over-estimated. After all, millions of years of evolution mean that prey fish are well adapted to detect and evade their predators, with smaller fishes particularly alert to threats from above such as fish-eating birds. Though 'BB' was talking of his observations of sticklebacks in the following extract from the chapter *The Fishes' Element* from his *The Fisherman's Bedside Book* (1943), the lesson is as pertinent when approaching all coarse fishes:

"This surely shows that their sight is very keen especially when there is any movement at a higher level than themselves. It is natural that this should be so. The kingfishers always have their places on an upper bough, and for uncounted centuries fish have come to suspect danger from above. Even a bird flying over the pool sends every fish down, and in that case, there can be no vibrations transmitted through the earth."

Specifically speaking of dace in English rivers, though written in his 1873 book *The Rod in India*, Henry Sullivan Thomas wrote that,

> *"It is well known to anglers that you may catch dace after dace out of a shoal till you have hooked and lost one in the landing, and that then you will ordinarily get no more dace out that shoal."*

Keep yourself but also your rod tip out of sight! Oh, and be careful of those heavy footfalls, clumsy casts and lost fish.

Specialist tackle for dace

This section needs little introduction, as there is no such thing as specialist dace tackle! I have already noted John Wilson's views (in his 1992 book *Catch Roach, Rudd and Dace*) that:

> *"Roach, rudd and dace are readily caught by the same techniques, on identical tackle and baits, often from the same locations, and in truth the angler is never quite sure which species will bite next…"*

To this, we added observations that 'Faddist' (Edward Ensom) covers angling for roach and dace within the same book (*Roach and Dace Fishing*), whilst John Bailey and Roger Miller address dace and chub together (in their 1990 book *Chub and Dace*) as does Henry Bell (in his undated *Fly-fishing for Chub and Dace*).

Other authors too have expressed the same sentiment about dace tackle and tactics. As another example, E. Marshall-Hardy wrote, in his 1942 *Coarse Fish*, that,

> *"TACKLE FOR DACE-FISHING need not be purchased specially. Any light rod combined with fine line and a gossamer cast will give good results and the greatest degree of sport when playing*

these lively fish. Most anglers use the same tackle for Roach, Chub, Rudd, Perch and Dace. All round lightness is, however, the secret of getting the best out of Dace fishing."

Arthur P. Bell too, in his 1930 book *Fresh-water Fishing for the Beginner*, adds to this by saying that,

"Ordinary roach tackle can be used for dace fishing, and the angler may please himself as to whether he will employ the roach pole or the Nottingham or Sheffield rod. A very effective method of dace fishing is to "swim down" a small red worm, gentle, or caddis grub on very light tackle and in fast running water. The strike must be instantaneous, for the dace is a very rapid biter and easy to miss. The "sink and draw" method of fishing previously described will often account for a number of dace in hot summer weather."

Peter Wheat, in his 1975 book *Catch More Dace*, adds to this with,

"There is nothing at all specialised about dace fishing tackle… The important thing about tackle, any tackle, is that it should function perfectly."

As the old saying goes, "*It's not what you got, it's the way that you use it!*" So how does thinking about the ecology of the dace help us think about how best to deploy our armoury of techniques and tackle to offer the optimal presentation of suitable bait once we have located the fish?

In the ideal world…

My first pound-plus dace was a lovely fish taken late in the coarse season in the mid-1980s on a single grain of free-lined sweetcorn. It was the perfect way to take a wild dace. Well, nearly wild anyhow. The venue was the lower reach of the

River Beane in Hertfordshire, not far above where it joins the River Lea at Hartham Common. The Beane is a classic dace river, or at least was in those days, and has produced many decent specimens for at least the last century (see later in this book) and probably a lot longer than that prior to the keeping of such records. I say that the fish was 'nearly wild' for the simple reason that Hartham Common was popular with dog-walkers and pedestrians, and so stalking individual fish in the shallow, clear waters was just a little easier than a truly wild fish in a remote location as they were used to a certain level of human movement.

The same is also true of dace in stretches of river bordering pasture, where cattle movement can to some degree inure them to bank-side movement. But these River Beane fish were still flighty and required the angler to use all available cover to get close enough for a cast, and for the cast to be accurate and subtle with the rod low to the ground at all times if the dace were not to vanish downstream in an instant.

I had spotted some good fish, and a very good one in particular, when observing the stretch with polarised glasses from a high footbridge. Several nice, plump dace were hanging in mid-water in the clear, shallow waters, evidently intercepting the odd morsel brought to them by the current. I then had the task of clambering through some low bushes by the river, keeping both my silhouette and that of my rod below the horizon, to reach a point that allowed me to cover the fish.

First of all, I lay the rod down and concentrated on flicking grains of corn out into the flow. This was nothing heavy-handed; just two or three grains every thirty seconds or so. Initially, there was no response from the dace, which in itself was a good thing as the sound of foreign objects hitting the water ahead and then sailing past them on the current can be enough to induce panic. Within a minute or two, some of the dace had started to veer across the current to intercept the tasty yellow grains. Strangely, for a bait so different to anything that they might encounter in the wild, sweetcorn can have an instant appeal for many fish from grayling to dace and roach to carp. Some people suggest that this is because they resemble fish eggs, though I think that unlikely as they don't smell like them and are a great deal bigger.

When the fish were intercepting my free offerings confidently, it was time to try a baited hook. Subtlety was the key. A float trotted through the crystalline shallows would have signalled danger, and the splash of a ledger, even a fine rig weighted with only a swan shot, would not only have alerted the fish but also dragged the bait down below feeding level. The answer was to offer the bait *au naturel*.

This was 'one chance' fishing; any unnatural movement of the bait would send the shoal fleeing for cover. However, luck and patience had stacked the odds in my favour. I focused on the precise position where I knew, from watching the free offerings, a grain must fall if it were to be intercepted by my chosen specimen. The cast had to be accurate. Too far upstream and the pull of current on line would have dragged the bait unnaturally off course. A cast too close to the fish would have spooked it. I hooked a single grain of corn onto a size 12 gold hook tied directly through to greased 2lb line, lobbing it out with an underhand flick of my 12 foot fibreglass rod to land among a few loose-fed grains thrown with my free hand.

As the yellow grain drifted in the current past the largest dace in the shoal, the fish veered from its station just sufficiently to engulf it. And, with a lift of the rod, I felt that characteristic, shimmering fight of a sturdy dace. The other fish scattered instantly, but that did not matter now as I steered the struggling fish on the light line, hands 'soft' on the rod to avert pulling out the hook or straining the light line, and within a few moments the platinum bar lay in the folds of my net.

What a gorgeous prize!

Not only had I slipped a net under my first true specimen dace, lured wholly and satisfyingly by design, but I had caught her in the purest possible manner. It had all the mystique of stalking visible trout with the dry fly, albeit it with neither the expense nor the bullshit that tends to go with that! The anticipation of spotting the fish, coaxing it to accept my offerings, presenting it a single grain on free-line then striking by sight was a marvellous experience in itself. How much more pure can it get?

Most of my other dace fishing is fairly crude by comparison! So, since we don't live every day in the 'ideal world' but instead inhabit the murkier waters of the 'real world' – snags, turbid waters, unseen quarry, line-snatching wind and all! – it is worth saying a few words on presenting to dace in less idyllic circumstances.

Matching the Conditions

The free-line featured heavily in my early angling days. As a lad throughout the 1960s, 'dapping' (as we called it) for dace, chub and roach with merely a baited hook to line was a favourite method. It is still the purest way of taking fish.

Then, throughout the early 1970s, as I made a slow metamorphosis from random fisherman to specimen angler, free-lining remained a favoured method in the waters I fished. These waters were mainly neglected farm ponds, quiet estate lakes, brick pits and small rivers, the only kind accessible to me as I rode my bike

round Sussex. But they were suited well to the subtle, close range approach of the free-line, often fishing for visible fish. This apprenticeship of specimen fishing in a county then largely a desert for specimen fish taught me well about the need for a subtle approach, and the hours spent observing fish and their reaction to my baits and their presentation remain etched into my consciousness as much as all my subsequent research and work in the aquatic environments of the world.

A somewhat younger author joins the big league with a (poorly photographed) 15 ounce dace from the upper reaches of the River Arun in Sussex.

I had luck, taking some genuinely big fish for the calibre of waters to which

I had access. Both roach and rudd over the two-pound barrier fell frequently to my free-lined offerings in forgotten pools, estate lakes and tributaries, mainly on breadflake, and dace too of up to 15 ounces from the sinuous little River Arun in the years before a dreadful pollution incident nearly wiped out the fish stocks of the upper river in the early 1970s.

But free-lining is only one technique, and only applies to dace fishing in some waters and conditions. Consistent capture of specimen dace from different waters depends instead on learning to adapt techniques to ensure that the bait one offers reaches the dace where they are and in a way that is acceptable to them.

To amplify this point about the appropriateness of tackle for presentation, I should note that I have taken other specimen dace on really hefty tackle – big floats carrying up to five swan shot – and done so entirely by design. The reason for this is quite simply that, in the wrong circumstances, too much finesse is a complete killer!

For example, when the river is up and coursing through, without a really hefty float that can carry bulk weights adequate to reach the stiller layers of water near the river bed, and be held back hard against the more rapid surface flow such that the bait moves at the more genteel pace of these deep layers, your bait will likely be nowhere near the fish or else be dragged through at an unnaturally fast pace. More on this later, but the watchword here is *appropriateness*. Finesse for its own sake can turn off many more fish than it will turn on.

Raking, wading and ground-baiting with cows

It is well-documented that the old 'Thames Professionals' and other guides of Victorian and Edwardian angling parties would often rake the bed of the river to attract gudgeon. However, the same was also true of dace fishing parties, dace once being a popular target for this type of 'social' fishing enterprise, with the species attracted to the mist of silt and small creatures stirred up from the river bed. William J. Howes, in his 1958 book *Dace: How to Catch Them*, commended this method too, stating that,

> "*Raking the river bed well above the swim helps to get the dace interested in feeding. I realise that many anglers would never consider trying this, but you can take it from me that on a suitable river it definitely works! Raking dislodges all kinds of insects and they get carried down with the stream, so the best hook-bait to use with this natural ground-baiting is caddis grubs and freshwater shrimps.*"

Many of us know that, notwithstanding the horrendous siltation and pollution issues that can result where cattle too freely enter watercourses and trample the bank, the activities of these large grazers can attract fish of several species, notably including dace. W. E. Davies notes, in his 1971 (5th edition) book *The Technique of Freshwater Fishing and Tackle Tinkering*, that,

> "*Dace in particular like streamy water which has been disturbed by cattle.*"

However, if one is concerned about too much ecological damage resulting from raking the bed of the river or 'ground-baiting with cows', a simpler and equally effective expedient is to fish for dace in shallower waters when wading. Regular movement of your feet will send puffs of suspended silt and small creatures down the current, to the general excitation of any dace residing there. You can even do this to stimulate dace in deeper waters by fishing from any shallow run into the deeper section.

Do be aware though that dace are acutely sensitive to pressure waves travelling through water. These are broadly similar to the sensations that we know as sound or vibration, but magnified many times since water transmits sound nearly five times faster than air. Any kind of clue we give them by way of pressure waves will be picked up efficiently. So wade carefully and, always an important consideration when wading and particularly so in streamier water, do so safely.

The dace angler afloat

Whether to present the fly or to offer a trotted float, some anglers enjoy a day afloat. Of course, this will generally be unnecessary where dace will be found taking flies in shallow waters. But, there are still a few surviving 'Thames Professionals' who offer days out on a punt moored in the river. This is a superbly enjoyable way of taking fish of all species, though the would-be boat dace angler has to be very aware of three things.

Firstly, be well organised; it is easy to lose or trample tackle in the narrow confines of a boat! Secondly, be quiet; with steady feeding you may bring fish right up to and beneath the boat where any sound-waves from clumsy movements will betray you directly. Thirdly, be safe; only go out with experienced boatmen, and ensure that you wear a life jacket. On this latter point, one should really wear such a life-preserver when wading, though few of us, myself included, have the wisdom and common sense to routinely heed my sound advice! In the modern era of big and fast pleasure boats, positioning yourself out of the main 'highway' of the river is also prudent, as is ensuring that you do not leave yourself too vulnerable to wash from passing boat traffic.

The fishing punt, still seen on the Thames but sadly relegated to history on rivers such as the Hampshire Avon and many besides, would traditionally be anchored fore and aft either with ropes (chains being too noisy) or attached to two long staves, or 'ryepecks', driven into the soft silt on the river bed.

Other types of boat may be used, though these are so diverse that it makes no sense to offer further specific guidance here. Whatever you do, safety first!

Other notes on safety

Since we have mentioned the paramount importance of safety on boats, let's also quickly address other aspects of safety whilst presenting baits to dace.

These are reminders of issues that should be second-nature, and which are covered more exhaustively in other publications.

Beware of using conductive materials, particularly long carbon rods and poles, near overhead power lines. If in doubt, avoid these areas, and if you don't understand why then ask someone who does about the dangers not just from direct contact with the wires but also the possibility of electrical currents arcing through damp air. Likewise, it is better to have a blank session at home than to risk waving those conductive 'lightening rods' around during a lightening storm, earthed as you will be by damp clothes in contact with the ground! Buoyancy is something about which we are all too cavalier. But don't go afloat without a life preserver that can buoy you up if you fall in, dragged down by saturated weatherproof clothing. The same principle should apply to us all when we wade, particularly in deeper or faster water, as well as when venturing too close to the river bank in uncertain conditions such as when snow or ice obscures the edge. You have been warned!

The fighting dace

Now, let's be clear on this point. You don't need to strap yourself to a fighting chair for dace, nor will they straighten any but the absolutely worst made hooks! However, for their size, dace are game fighters, and on occasions may need some special handling.

E. Marshall-Hardy, a former editor of the much-missed *Angling* magazine, says of the fight of a dace in his 1963 (much revised late edition) book *Angling Ways*,

> *"They are sprightly and sporting fish which will fight every inch from the 'strike' to the 'net'. It is a pity they are so comparatively small... I have often thought that, weight for weight, there is no more game fish. The speed with which they take a bait has much to attract the angler, and the fisherman who can 'hit' four out of seven 'dace snatches' may pride himself on his skill and speed."*

On light tackle, the dace is a game fighter indeed! And, in addition to being often very fast biters which are hard to hook, they are pretty adept too at twisting themselves off the hook on the retrieve. They achieve this by their lively fight, which causes them to spin in the water on the retrieve. So bear this in mind and, if obstructions around the swim allow, play the dace gently on 'soft hands' so that they do not spin madly against too strong a pull. There is another good reason for giving dace their head. They will often be hooked in shallow water, and a dace bursting through the surface in panic is a sure-fire method for scaring a shoal which will either bolt from the shallows or cease to feed. David Carl Forbes puts it eloquently in his 1966 book *Small Stream Fishing*,

> *"It has truly been said that nothing travels faster under water than fear, and this might well be an adage to keep in mind when fishing – particularly in confined spaces."*

For smaller dace, it is often least stressful for the fish and the best way to avoid disturbing a shoal to swing the fish out of the water and to hand in as quick and smooth a motion as possible. This is particularly so in shallow water or smaller streams, and when pike are drawn to the attractive sight of struggling fish and to lunge at every fish you hook!

So what methods should I use?

Having dealt with the generality of *presentation*, and a few odds and ends about dace angling to further inform our thinking and enjoyment, it is time now to look at some of the methods we may deploy to catch more and/or bigger dace.

Free-line, float and ledger

There are many methods for presenting bait to a dace. Free-line, float and ledger cover many of them and, with their numerous variants, form the subject of this chapter.

Free-lining (again)

I know I have eulogised free-lining as a fun and subtle way of taking dace already. However, at the risk of boring you senseless, let me reiterate that it is the method *par excellence* when you can get away with it.

You need no sophisticated tackle. A rod of twelve feet long is ideal, a compromise that is long enough to give you 'reach' yet short enough that the line does not tend to 'stick' too badly to the blank. I like old (unfashionable) glass fibre float rods for this type of presentation, as the old-style chromed stand-off rings allow the light bait to be cast freely and there is less blank against which the line might stick. In wet conditions, I might smear a little Vaseline on the upper section of the rod if 'line sticking' becomes a problem. Glass fibre rods also provide an excellent through-action, with none of the unforgiving 'locking up' that can afflict some carbon fibre blanks.

Pretty much any free-casting fixed-spool reel will do, provided it is free enough on the backwind or clutch to absorb the first lunge of the dace (or the big chub that may just muscle in first!) If you are brave and practiced enough, a centrepin reel will serve well too, cast 'Nottingham style' (pulling loops of line from between the rod rings before casting).

Line and hook... it doesn't get much simpler.

The line I favour for this subtle stalking approach is 2lb; brand of your choice but do ensure that it is both supple and resistant to abrasion. Braids are to be avoided like the plague because, strong though they are for their diameter, they are highly visible to fish in this primarily visual form of fishing. For this reason, fluorocarbon lines can be an asset as they 'vanish' into the water though, in practice, I have not found them superior to a pale or translucent nylon monofilament which costs substantially less. No need for a finer tippet, and for four reasons: firstly, the knot can betray you in the water; secondly, it can trap algae or weed; thirdly, it can create a weak link; and fourthly, 2lb reel line straight through offers less resistance to casting. However, what I will do is always grease the line by reeling it back through a tissue daubed with a little Vaseline, which allows the line to float and also helps prevent it sticking to a damp rod on casting and when playing out line. Finish this off with a hook, light and fine-wired so as not to adversely affect the behaviour of the bait in the water and anything from a size 12 to a size 18 according to bait size, and there you have it!

What is a lot more important than precisely what tackle you use is how you use it. I have already indicated the need for a subtle approach to stalking. You generally have to get close to the fish without spooking them, as you will usually be fishing for them by sight and casting at them with a very light bait. At other times, you may be casting to a spot that your watercraft tells you is distinctly worth a try. On these occasions, watch for the sudden disappearance of the bait as it falls through the water, and strike on sight. Or, if the water is a little turbid, watch the floating line at the point where it vanishes underwater and strike at any sudden or unexpected movement which is likely to indicate a fish intercepting the free-falling offering.

A little tip here is that you can crinkle a little of the line between your fingers at the point where it is likely to disappear. This improves its visibility to help you spot subtle 'takes' from the unseen fish below.

The free-lining method can be used to present pretty much any bait you desire. From hemp to maggots, tares and casters, luncheon meat and worms, caddis larvae and elderberries, freshwater shrimps and sweetcorn, bread and baked beans, all can be offered thus with the utmost subtlety. Obviously, the lighter baits can not be flicked quite so far as their heavier counterparts. However, some baits can be weighted naturally to aid casting without damaging their natural behaviour once in the swim. For example, a large bob of breadflake can be dipped in the river (or a pot of water containing a drop or two of flavouring) then cast straight away before it has softened sufficiently to fly off the hook. This is a method I favoured and used extensively to lure wary dace and rudd in the 1970s, with relatively prodigious casts of perhaps thirty yards becoming quite feasible with practice on balanced tackle. Another trick is to use, say, maggots but to cover the baited hook with a large, loose piece of breadflake that adds casting ballast but is then 'struck off' the hook once the bait lands in the desired spot.

If you want a really relaxing day on the water, covering many miles with the minimum of tackle, then it is worth putting several types of bait, a few spare hooks and some spools of line of different thickness into your pocket and taking off with free-line rod in hand. Fishing by sight, you might start by flicking out maggots for dace in the fast runs, upping the line to say four or five pounds where the current drops off and the chub lurk, beefing up again to trundle meat or worms for barbel lurking beneath the *Ranunculus* in moderate glides, scaling down again to offer breadflake to intercept roach feeding in mid-water where the gentler currents prevail, before once again finding dace accepting casters in the lively water at the tail of the next weir downstream. The old-fashioned glass fibre float rod will handle all these line strengths and fish admirably. A better day will be hard to find, netting you a diversity of fish and very probably some better, tackle-shy specimens too, as well as teaching you more about fish location and behaviour than years sat behind a static float!

The big enemy for the free-line fisher is drag, be that from wind or current. Once the bait starts to get pulled about, its unnatural movements will work against you. So it is as important to know when not to use free-line as it is to know when to use it. You will generally get only a short 'trotting length' from a free-lined bait and if this is not enough to cover feeding fish, you might resort to other methods for the extra control you seek.

The 'twisted twig'

On occasions when a slightly longer cast or better visual indication is needed, and there is not the time to change the rig, I modify this approach a little further by attaching a short twig or matchstick to the line at that point with a clove hitch. A short section cut from a coloured rubber band can also serve this purpose, as well as making a serviceable stop for a sliding float and ledger rig. Short sections of twig, reed or other suitable bank-side materials are fine. The clove hitch is an easy little knot providing a lazy means for turning the rig temporarily into a light, natural-material float rig that is quick to adapt and then again to remove.

The clove hitch is a simple but really useful angling knot, here as a 'twisted twig'.

Obviously, this 'twisted twig' method gives you a clearer visual signal of attention at the business end of your line, but you should be striking on sight of the bait vanishing or the line above it moving. Natural though the 'float' may appear, beware an over-large stick which will create excessive resistance to a taking fish and which may also spook them as it moves on the surface on the 'take' or strike. Another tip is to ensure that you secure the clove hitch knot at only one end of the twig, such that a taking fish will upend and pull it under rather than try to drag the whole stick width-ways under the water. Oh, and do check the twig for sharp edges which may damage the line; that precaution covered, it can be done, undone and redone repeatedly without weakening the line.

I should add that this is a 'quick and dirty' method, but what it lacks in refinement it pays back to you handsomely in immediacy of response to a sighted fish. However, if it is too crude for your sensibilities, you might like instead to carry a light self-cocking waggler in your pocket to clip onto the line at a moment's notice.

Another variant upon this, where distance is not the issue but detection or the avoidance of line drag may be, is to cast the line over a floating leaf, twig or other obstacle and to use this as a handy temporary float. Not pretty, but very effective on its day in giving you just a tad more control against surface drag!

Controlling the bait

As we have said before, not every time you go fishing will you encounter the kind of idyllic river conditions that suit the presentation of free-lined baits by sight. In the 'real world', it gets too windy or the water is excessively turbulent or murky. However, we must recall that the dace is above all the *Prince of the Stream*, adept at and evolved to intercept baits at all depths in moving water. All other methods then, to one degree or another, just give us degrees more control over the presentation of bait and ensuing bite detection.

The free-line, or at least the line and hook, is the backbone around which all other fishing methods are applied simply to extend the effectiveness of bait presentation in different river conditions. The line and hook still forms the backbone of any alternative technique, no matter how sophisticated. This extensive overview of the diversity of free-line tactic does rather emphasise the fact that the line and hook together are the most important elements of fishing for dace, as indeed any fish, and that they should be of good and reliable quality, well-maintained to avoid unnecessary failures, knotted with appropriate knots tied carefully and wetted before tightening to avoid friction-induced weaknesses.

The tackle and techniques we adopt to achieve that end are secondary to this prime objective; remember that to help you select the best method, think primarily of the behaviour of the bait in relationship to the natural behaviour of the fish. In the remainder of this chapter, we'll be looking at how various forms of float fishing (waggler, stick, loafer/Avon and pole) and ledgering can help us achieve that end.

'Sink and draw'

Before we leave the topic of free-lined baits entirely, it is worth mentioning another method discussed by the authors of some older angling books. A 'sink and draw' approach is sometimes seen advocated for dace as well as for roach and other more active silver fish. This is a variant upon the free-line methods discussed above. It is basically a weight-assisted method for presenting a bait in a current, and is one that I have occasionally found successful in circumstances when mainstream float or ledger tactics are too clumsy but unaided free-line fishing is impossible. There is a range of methods, and I will start with the neutral-bouyancy methods advocated by Arthur P Bell in his 1930 book *Fresh-water Fishing for the Beginner*,

> *"During the hot summer months when the rivers are mostly running gin clear there are two methods of fishing which will frequently bring success when all other usual means fail. The first is known, for reasons which will be obvious, as "the Sink and Draw" method. The bait used is a caddis grub (obtainable from most tackle dealers) and the tackle required is a No. 10 hook attached to a fine-drawn gut cast three yards in length. Just above the hook loop attach one medium-sized shot, then before attaching the running line to the cast take a small piece of cork (a thin slice of a medicine bottle cork will fill the bill admirably) and thread the line through it. This done, attach the line to the cast and fix the cork to the line by plugging it with a small piece of match stick. It should be fixed sufficiently far up the line to enable the bait to reach the bottom whatever the depth.*

> *"When the angler has baited his hook he should walk quietly along the river bank casting his line into likely-looking weed runs or holes. The bait will sink very slowly and trickle, as it were, through the weeds. Frequently the bait is taken before it reaches the bottom. If not the angler should pause a little while*

and then raise his rod very slowly, at the same time gradually winding in his line. This is a most fascinating game, and will sometimes allow a man to "wipe the eye" of his brother anglers. It may be added here that roach are not the only fish which will fall victim to this deadly clear-water method, for perch, dace, chub, and even small jack are frequently taken."

William J. Howes, in his 1958 book *Dace: How to Catch Them*, adds to this in describing his simpler method thus,

"After several fish have been taken, a change to Sink-and-Draw may be worth while for there might be a few larger dace swimming deep at the tail of the shoal. The first thing is to change the hook for one of a larger size. Fix a small weight about 18 inches above the hook. The hook may be baited with either maggots, red worm, or the tail or head end of a lobworm.

"The weight will assist in making an over-head cast, and help the tackle to sink. Raising the rod-top will draw in the bait a yard or so where it is allowed to sink again. The manoeuvre is repeated until the tackle is retrieved. Cast out again to a fresh position and repeat the sinking and drawing movements. A bite will be recognised by a pull on the line."

Though somewhat different, this method has some similarities to the description in Izaac Walton's *The Compleat Angler*,

"Next, let me tell you, you shall fish for this Roach in Winter, with paste or gentles; in April, with worms or cadis; in the very hot months, with little white snails; or with flies under water, for he seldom takes them at the top, though the Dace will. In many of the hot months, Roaches may also be caught thus: take a May-fly, or ant-fly, sink him with a little lead to the bottom, near to the piles or posts of a bridge, or near to any

posts of a weir, I mean any deep place where Roaches lie quietly, and then pull your fly up very leisurely, and usually a Roach will follow your bait up to the very top of the water, and gaze on it there, and run at it, and take it, lest the fly should fly away from him.

"I have seen this done at Windsor and Henley Bridge, and great store of Roach taken; and sometimes, a Dace or Chub."

Floating away

And so we turn to various methods of presenting bait to dace under a float. But, before, we launch into the technicalities, let's just reflect a moment on the joy of float fishing. Much has been written about the float, so to introduce this section I will turn to one of the masters of angling writing. Hugh Tempest Sheringham wrote many beautiful and illuminating words about angling in general, and very many of these in particular about floats for which he clearly had a keen interest and passion. He thought carefully about suiting floats to specific purposes, but also about taking account of their inherent beauty and appreciation. The following, from his 1910 book An *Open Creel*, is typical.

"For I readily admit that virtue lies almost wholly in using the right float. Shape is important, and so is colour, and it is pleasant at times to dally with material. I have heard many learned disputations on the respective merits of quills from different birds, one man favouring swan, another goose, a third peacock, and each maintaining his opinion with epic accounts of past sport. But as a rule these disputants are a shade too practical; their floats are for use only, and they make no allowance for the element of beauty which should have its place in the consideration."

So then, let us consider float tactics to tackle the sprightly dace.

Offering the waggler

The next logical step to the free-line or the impromptu 'twisted twig', in terms of offering a bait that will tumble naturally in a shallow flow, is to employ waggler float tactics. I am using the term 'waggler' in its broadest sense here to cover all floats which attach to the line bottom-end-only. There is a bewildering multiplicity of bottom-end-only floats – peacocks, inserts, duckers, zoomers and so forth – which I will mention where it makes significant difference. But with a float there is a significant element of aesthetic pleasure rather than 'hard' science so I'll gloss over minor differences in float types, the choice of which is unlikely to have any real impact on fishing for dace.

Wagglers come in all sorts of shapes, sizes, materials and modifications, suiting them to a diversity of applications.

The bottom-end-only attachment does mean that the line, at least immediately above the float, is sunk and also that resistance on the line from either above or below the water line will pull the float beneath the surface. This helps presentation when the sunken line escapes the clutches of surface currents or wind, though in stronger flows the opposite effect may result as the sunken line is at the mercy of turbulent water which may compromise both presentation and bite detection.

Nevertheless, the waggler serves many needs when tracking down dace. Unlike most top-and-bottom attached floats, the waggler can be presented effectively upstream. This is particular handy both for casting up into the turbulent waters of weir pools, and also when fishing wilder rivers where the best, or only possible, 'angle of attack' to a favoured run of water is from downstream. Furthermore, it is excellent for presenting a free-falling bait on an unweighted line beneath the float, exploring the depths of a river at which fish just may be feeding. This also suits it ideally for those more scarce stillwater dace, where the bait is on the end of a long unweighted, or sparsely-shotted, 'tail' of line that takes some time to sink naturally through the water column. Either that, or the shot can be spaced along the line to favour a particular depth at which you have found fish feeding in either still or flowing waters. This capacity to offer a free-falling bait suits those particles that dace might expect to find sinking or suspended naturally in the water column, such as hemp, tares, maggots, casters, sweetcorn, caddis and other 'natural' baits, and so forth.

Remember that dace can be feeding at any depth and will often rise in the water column to feed. As Kenneth W. Clower puts it in his lively little 1962 book *Fishing Famous Rivers: Hampshire Avon*,

> *"It should be kept well in mind that, during the early part of the season, Avon roach, dace and chub in particular will often feed well off the bottom, taking their fill of the natural food on the weeds or carried down through the runs in the fast stream."*

The waggler excels in shallow waters, cast upstream or downstream, allowing the bait to tumble with the current with minimal constraint. Also, for searching out the streamy runs between beds of submerged water plants, a waggler can be a subtle way of presenting a free-falling bait amid a catapult-full of free offerings; a very effective way of taking dace. Another advantage to the waggler is that it pops below the surface when you strike or retrieve line, particularly when you deliberately plunge the rod tip below the river's surface to ensure no disturbance of the river's surface, avoiding the inevitable splash and bow-waves that result from striking and retrieving top-and-bottom floats against a current.

I also often favour the waggler for trotting deeper rivers when the current is not too strong, generally selecting a relatively large float (from 3AAA to 3 SSG) that has a good deal of the weight already loaded on the base of the float and ideally equipped with a device that locks the float to the line. In the absence of a self-locking type of waggler, the established method is to lock the float at the desired depth with a large shot either side, although continued flexing can weaken the line and neither is it quite so easy to change depth. Either that, or lock the float with a pair of small rubber ledger stops which, though better than the shot (for self-weighted floats at least) do tend to slip with repeated casting. Whatever your chosen method of attaching the waggler and its bulk weights, the remaining shot can be spaced as conditions determine, either close to the float for exploring water depths or spaced down the line to target a particular feeding depth. For deeper water fishing, I generally under-shot a float set over-depth, the longer amount of float sticking out above the surface not only providing better visibility in failing light but enabling the float to be held back somewhat without diving wholly under the surface or else being tugged underwater as the bait bounces along the irregular bed profile of a fancied swim. Finished off with a lighter hooklength relative to the (generally 2½-3lb) reel line and a hook of a size suitable to the bait, you are ready to fish. If you worry about the crudity of the waggler method I describe for deeper water, don't fret. I have taken pound-plus dace and three-pound-plus roach on the method so it seems to work OK!

A big waggler also excels where there is a fierce wind blowing down the river, when traditional top-and-bottom floats tend to get blown off course. This is due to the line between rod tip and float being largely sunk and so evading the surface drag. The ducker is a squat variant of the waggler generally recommended for these downstream wind circumstances.

Giving them some stick

By contrast, the stick float is attached 'top and bottom' to the reel line, the float itself is generally unweighted although some wire- or Perspex-stemmed models offer a little weight at the bottom of the float that can improve stability in the river and 'cut' through the water on striking. There are many types of stick float, from the stemmed varieties noted above to straight balsa sticks, floats of extruded plastic with long or short tips, and so the list goes on. The once-ubiquitous quill float, be that from a bird or porcupine, is another type of float that can be most effectively used for trotting as a stick float.

For most applications, largely dictated by current and wind strength, fishing depth and required casting distance, stick floats range in size from 5x No.8 to 5AAA shot, though they can be bought (or made) bigger or smaller than that. I will not cover them all here, but discuss the method in general terms and its applicability to different river conditions in more detail.

Diverse forms of stick float match different river conditions.

Sticks excel in rivers of moderate flow but which are not too deep. Fished from a centrepin or small fixed spool reel, either open-face or closed-face, stick floats offer effective bait control and sensitive presentation in a broad range of river conditions. The stick is, however, less effective at distance, though ideal at not more than a rod length or two from the bank. A rod as short as twelve feet will suffice with thirteen feet a commonly-used length, allowing the line to travel freely to the pull of the relatively light float. For stick float fishing in heavier weather, when the water is too shallow or slack to use an Avon or loafer float, I favour my fifteen foot rods for better control though I will sometimes break out a twenty-foot rod when the stick float offers the best presentation during high winds.

It is certainly worth greasing the line – I use Vaseline on a piece of tissue through which the reel line is wound back – to allow the line to float, all the better to evade the clutches of surface current that might otherwise drag your float off course.

Stick float fishing enables you to fish at a fixed depth, and within reason to vary that depth on the trot by holding back the line slightly such that the shotted line and bait flutters up in the water column although this should not be overdone as otherwise unnatural movements will turn fish off the bait. When trotting using any method, we have to remember the phenomenon of *laminar flow*. Judged by surface currents or the movements of suspended matter in the surface layers of water, the river may seem to be flowing at a swift pace. Yet, even in the most turbulent flows, frictional resistance at the river bed, particularly where there are bed irregularities or sunken obstructions, creates a narrow static or slower-moving layer which offers small invertebrates protection as they forage for food. More genteel flows occur above this, with the strongest flows in the centre and surface of the river far away from hard surfaces, obviously except where currents scour the outer edge of a tight bend. Currents at depth are therefore generally a lot slower than the apparent pace of the river, and so trotted baits have to be held back to varying degrees to ensure that the bait not only proceeds somewhere beneath the float but also does so at a rate that would be natural for free offerings at that depth.

Shotting pattern can affect the effectiveness of bait presentation. Commonly, stick floats are shotted 'shirt button' style, or in other words with the shot spaced evenly up the line. However, in more turbulent flows, it is advantageous to bulk the shot further down the line to get the bait down to the feeding depth quickly, ensuring a 'tail' of unweighted line below the bottom shot such that the bait itself can move naturally. On some occasions, and particularly when the fish are taking baits 'on the drop', you may decide to bulk up the shot closer to the stick float, although often the waggler may offer better presentation in these circumstances. For all these methods, shotting pattern, like stick float type and size, should be dictated by the river conditions and fish location. Smaller and lighter float will, in the main, offer less splash on the strike and wake on the retrieve.

Dumpy, gaudy-topped, cork-bodied floats on stick spindles may have been favourites when I was a schoolboy but, due to their resistance to taking fish, they generally have no place in sensitive presentation to dace. Generally, that is. The exception is the dumpy 'grayling floats', presented like a stick float, which can rule supreme when trotting shallow, broken flows.

Loafing down the river

When flows get stronger, or else there is a need to get bait down to a deeper feeding depth rapidly in moving water, the Avon or 'loafer' styles of float come into their own. This is the classic method of long trotting (or 'swimming down' or 'tight corking' as the method was once widely known), holding back a float as it runs down with the stream.

Trotting a heavy float down a strongly-flowing winter river is one of the forms of fishing that gives me the greatest pleasure, particularly when using a centrepin for fine line control. For these river conditions, a heavier float is necessary both so that it can carry adequate weight to keep the bait down deep in the water but also to provide you with adequate resistance for holding back the float hard, enabling the bait to progress down the river at the slower pace of deeper layers of water. This entails using Avon or 'loafer' (or 'chubber') style floats.

The primary difference between these types of float is that the Avon float has a pronounced buoyant body with a cane, wire, quill or plastic stem extension beneath, whereas the 'loafer' float comprises basically the dumpy upper body with a minimal extension below. In bygone years, highly effective 'loafer' floats were made from the thick end of a swan's primary wing feathers, the bottom extension comprising a glued-in section of whittled balsa or other buoyant wood; there is no reason why the enterprising DIY aficionado couldn't still do this although the modern plastic floats are more durable. Personally, I often use 'Bolognese'-type floats for this type of trotting, due to the stability and visibility of this type of float and the improved 'cut' of the long wire stem through the water on striking.

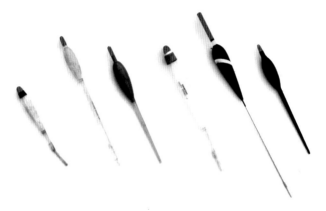

Heavy Avon, 'loafer' and 'Bolognese' floats are ideal for heavy flows and long trotting.

These methods are for strong flows through which your line needs to cut, so we are talking big-bodied floats. Anything that takes between two-and-a-half to five swan shot (and occasionally more) will be adequate; when river conditions suggest a finer float then the stick float approach is almost certainly more appropriate unless you need the weight of a big float to counteract wind. To ensure that the bait sinks quickly to the desired depth and that it remains beneath the float rather than billowing out downstream in stronger currents, some form of bulk shot is required down the line. Many people use a chain of large shot for this, although I find that these can weaken the line as they flex against each other. Metallic rubber tube-shot is suitable, stopped at the bottom end with a split shot. However, my favoured method is to use a black-painted masonry nail attached to the reel line top-and-bottom with short lengths of rig tubing. Commercial olivettes or even small drilled ledger weights are favoured by other anglers.

A half-metre or less below the bulk shot, a 'dropper shot' should be attached to the line immediately above the weaker hook length. I favour a hefty BB shot, though a No.4 and sometimes a lot lighter shot are more common. This keeps the bait close to the bed of the river or your chosen feeding depth, moderating somewhat the effect of the bulk weight and allowing the bait to dribble more naturally with the slower currents. Hook size will be dictated by bait, and in turn the precise breaking strains of reel line and hook length should be matched to conditions. Vaseline treatment of the line above the float is a great advantage, as already explained for stick float fishing.

A centrepin reel is ideal for this type of fishing, feeding off the line evenly as it rotates and also giving you a direct 'feel' on the strike, fight and retrieve. The centrepin has, in fact, seen something of a renaissance in recent years, though for me it never went away! A fixed spool reel can be used, but it is best to use a model with a bale arm that can be closed manually so that you don't 'bounce' off any fish in the moment of slack line before an automatic bale arm snaps shut. A longer rod is best-suited to controlling line and setting the hook at distance – I find that a fifteen foot rod is ideal – as well as controlling the fish better on the fight and keeping them out from undercut banks near the landing net.

Trotting for dace from the centrepin in heavy flows on the River Wye; heaven!

Fishing the static float

Since dace are essentially creatures of flowing water, I find that static fishing methods using the float are not often required. Exceptions to this might be in those few docks, lakes, canals and other unusual habitats in which they sometimes prosper, and of course also the times of year – mainly in the dead of winter – when the fish might move into deeper slacks where shoals of roach and chub also lie. In these unusual still or slow water circumstances, you might consider the merits of tactics such as stret-pegging (or 'laying on'), float ledgering, or the 'lift method'.

I will, however, convey to you the specific guidance on 'stret-pegging' for dace as offered by William J. Howes in his 1958 book *Dace: How to Catch Them*,

"For a change of method we might try stret-pegging, providing the conditions are suitable. This is a style which usually calls for a deep swim fairly close to the bank with a medium or slow current. The float is a quill capable of carrying four or five average split-shot, and is adjusted to allow some 12 to 15 inches more than the depth of the swim.

"A small portion of ground-bait is thrown in, always bearing in mind the rule "little and often". The angler makes his cast and, holding his rod in front of him, trots the tackle 3 or 4 yards down the swim. It is then held there quite still whilst the action of the current causes the bait to rise off the bottom and waver about attractively. Dace often find this movement most enticing, and at times irresistible.

"However, if no bite is registered after a moment or two the float is worked down-stream a little farther and again it is checked. The angler can work his float all over the swim in this manner, and when a bite does come it will almost invariably be sharp and decisive."

There is, obviously, no ideal pole for dace fishing, although the general advice of buying as long and stiff a pole as your wallet and physique can bear holds good to maximise your 'reach' in tricky swims. Ensure that you can elasticate the top two sections, and do so with an elastic of around No.8 which combines the twin virtues of being adequately forgiving whilst giving you the muscle to ease the fish from between weed beds or across turbulent currents. For the more match-inclined or slighter-framed angler, a shorter whip of six or seven metres may also serve when conditions are favourable and the dace can be lured close in.

If you are remaining in a favoured swim and intend to feed the fish carefully to draw them to you or attract them to take your bait, ensure that you can sit comfortably either using a seat box or a chair that lets you take some of the weight of the pole over your knee. Otherwise, your back muscles will soon let you know all about the stresses and strains of counterbalancing, shipping and unshipping the pole all day. Or you may chose, as I most often do with the pole, to rove the river and pluck unwary fish from likely-looking and sometimes otherwise inaccessible holes and runs!

I have no specific pole float recommendations other than to suggest a pear-shaped body for moving waters and to ensure that the float can bear enough bulk weights, be they olivettes or shot, to carry the bait down to the right depth in the current. Stick and waggler floats can also be used with the pole when conditions dictate that form of bait presentation; indeed stick float under the whip was the downfall of one of the heaviest ever match bags of dace, as covered in the chapter dealing with *Giant bags and whopping great dace*. The lightest floats may appear to offer optimal sensitivity but, in practice, they don't give you adequate bait control in the kind of flows that dace like the best. Line and hook too should match conditions and bait. Again, it is best to err on the larger sizes if it is specimen dace that you are after. (A big dace can easily accommodate a size 12 hook, and I have taken them on hooks up to a No.2 as well when chubbing or barbel fishing with luncheon meat, though I don't recommend that as a first line of attack for dace!) For match angling, anything down to a size 22 may be more appropriate as dace can be extremely hook-shy on pressured waters.

Other than that, I will leave you to your own innovations, and the guidance of other specialist books on the subject of pole fishing as the method is hardly a mainstream specimen 'dace-killer'! Suffice to say that the usual cautionary notes about pulling for a break with the stretched elastic, and also pole care to avoid expensive breakages, apply no matter what fish you are hoping to catch on the method.

Ledgering

As we've concluded from looking at the biology of the dace, this is a fish adapted to sharper flows but also to feeding at all depths. So we can put aside the old tales we sometimes hear and read that the dace is a surface-feeder. Much of the time, they will act like trout and intercept morsels coming past them on the current. Also, like trout, they will feed on tasty items on the river bed. In the right conditions, ledgering (or legering) can be a most effective method for catching dace. I refer to a 'magic triple' in a later chapter of this book. I will leave you to discover what that means but, in the interim, just let me say that it was caught on ledger tactics as have been countless of my other specimen dace over the years.

When I was a lad (there, I've said it again!) during the early 1960s, the ledger was very much frowned upon as being for the idle; the so-called 'lazy man's way'. But times change and, in particular under the influence of both Richard Walker's and Peter Stone's writings (especially for me the latter's excellent 1963 book *Ledgering*), the finesse of ledgering came to be developed, known and exploited. This is hard to imagine these day, I know, when a generation of anglers has been brought up on dedicated ledger rods such as the quivertip, swingtip, feeder, and rods developed for static methods such as those used ubiquitously for carp angling.

Ledgering end-rigs are many and varied. The running ledger is the most basic, and perhaps the one that many of us grew up with. Here, the line runs through the ledger weight – be that a drilled 'bullet', coffin, torpedo-shaped lead or lead substitute – or else though a swivel embedded in the lead or lead substitute.

A favoured innovation of my own is to loop a swivel onto a short length of braid that is then superglued onto a stone of suitable size and of a colour that best matches it with the river bed; this is particularly useful for foreign angling when the weight premium of carrying too many proprietary ledger weights can be avoided.

Different types of ledger weights.

The lead is prevented from running freely to the hook by a stop, which may be a split shot, a knot, a swivel, a loop of line, a piece of rubber band or similar secured to the line with a clove hitch knot, a proprietary plastic stopper, or a rubber float stopper. (My favoured method is to use a short piece of rig tubing stoppered with a length of biodegradable spaghetti.) The lead holds the bait down on the river bed, and a taking fish pulls line through the weight which then registers as a bite on the rod tip, fingers or other indicator at the angler's end.

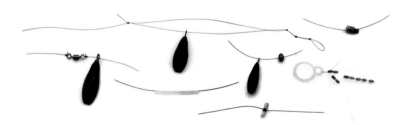

Different types of ledger stop.

The paternoster is another simple end rig, where the hook is tied to the main line and the weight is attached at the end of a dropper of line knotted onto the reel line. The fish can take and run with the bait, registering a bite before it tightens up against and feels the resistance of the weight.

Alternatively, in my favoured method, you can combine the virtues of both the running ledger and the paternoster by putting the ledger weight on a long 'dropper' which runs on the reel line. The weight is attached to one end of a length of heavier nylon, stiffer than the main reel line to help eliminate twisting and tangles, and a swivel is tied to the end. Both knots are masked by rig tubing. The reel line is passed through the swivel and stoppered – with a split shot, the rig tube and spaghetti that I have described, tying the swivel into a loop of reel line, or other suitable methods – and you have a sensitive method for bait presentation that will minimise resistance to a taking fish.

Of course, you can substitute the ledger weight itself for a swimfeeder (or 'feeder') which offers the fish free bait around the hook. There are many and varied types of swimfeeder, each appropriate to different river conditions and baits. A cage or mesh feeder, for example, excels for bread or cereal mixes, allowing them to break up as they sink, whilst a solid plastic feeder with drilled holes is best for maggots and similar baits that can escape gradually to create a tempting trickle of feed. Size, weight and style of feeder should be determined by the optimal presentation to fish. The splash of these so-called 'plastic pigs' into the water on casting should be a not inconsiderable element in your thinking about presentation!

Just some samples of the bewildering diversity of swimfeeders available.

Whatever the chosen method of ledgering, it goes without saying that reel line should be of appropriate strength. Tossing a heavy swimfeeder around all day can take its toll of frail lines so a durable brand of 4lb reel line should suffice for the small feeders best suited to the relatively slight appetites of dace. If you want to use a big swimfeeder, which you rarely should need for dace, then a beefier reel line will be required. Hooklength and hook type and size will be dictated by optimal presentation of bait.

As we have already touched upon, the methods for bite detection are many and varied. I will not cover them all here, nor over-burden you with fine details of the methods I cover as this is hardly helpful in the context of this little book. Again, I will return to the nature of the fish themselves for the underpinning guidance, as a number of facets of the structure and behaviour of dace are highly germane to choice of bite detection. Firstly, the streamlined, round-profiled body of the dace is adapted to swifter flows. This means that they are fast interceptors of food rather than species which tend to fin languidly around in static water mouthing bait for a long time.

Secondly, the mouth is relatively small, so the dace is unlikely to hold the bait in its mouth for a long time whilst it determines if it has found food or not. Add these two factors together, and they tell us that dace bite fast, which we all already know from experience! Thirdly, even a specimen dace is not a bulky fish. So, unlike burly carp or barbel, it is unlikely to embed itself on a hook through its own headlong charge when it feels the prick of a hook. This means that self-hooking 'bolt rigs' are also out. Whatever method we use has to absolutely minimise frictional resistance.

A once very popular but now sadly neglected method for tackling dace and other fish of stronger flows is the rolling ledger. This approach is relatively simple, comprising a straight ledger rig wherein the weight is just light enough, and ideally of a rounded shape such as a drilled bullet or an Arlesley bomb, to enable the current to move it along the river bed as if the bait were a free offering swept periodically by the current. It can be highly effective in places where float presentation is not possible, which can include not only under overhanging

Cage feeder, quivertip and fat female dace: a wonderful combination in winter flows.

vegetation but also in shallow water too far to cast by free-line but where a float may scare the fish. Bites are felt through the fingers, and a quick strike is necessary. In his 1958 book *Dace: How to Catch Them*, William J. Howes says of the technique that,

> "One of the reasons why it is so effective is its thoroughness, for even in a very swift stream the bait does not travel through the swim too quickly, and if used correctly a very wide area can be searched."

I have two 'hot favourite' methods of bite detection when ledgering for dace. Most sensitive by a long margin is touch ledgering, as the slightest quick nibble is felt instantly and, if one is holding the rod, can be responded to as promptly. It is also the perfect method when watching stars, chatting with visiting anglers, spotting fish or their rises and rolls, watching wrens or rodents work the river bank, or else just day-dreaming! Secondly, the quivertip is a very sensitive indicator if balanced finely with the pressure of flow on the end-tackle, registering both 'nods' and 'drop-backs' on the tip as fish pick up the bait. In both circumstances, hit the slightest tremble instantly.

The 'springtip' is a variant upon this, a spring attaching to the rod tip such that the whole 'tip' swivels on the end of the rod to register a bite. A well-balanced one can serve adequately, though personally I have not got on with them very well as casting distance and accuracy are compromised. At a pinch, you can watch the tip movement of a 'normal' float or ledger rod, but many dace bites will register too slowly or subtly against their greater resistance, although it is surprising just how powerfully a hungry specimen dace can thump round a rod tip!

There are various methods for attaching betalights (permanently fluorescent lights powered by weakly radioactive chemicals in a fine glass tube) or cheaper luminous chemical varieties (giving shorter-lived light when constituent chemicals are mixed) to the tip of a rod to maximise bite detection into the hours of darkness. You can tape them, glue them, whip in a piece of rig tubing to hold them or, my favourite method, unstick the tip ring and slide on a float adapter into which a betalight is inserted once the tip ring is glued back on. Either that, or aim a torch upwards onto the rod when it is in its rest. Provided it does not move, fish seem to accept a point of light on the bank provided it is not aimed down at them into the water.

A highly sensitive method that is today sadly underused is the swingtip, and this despite its effective deployment to take the British Record roach in March 2006. However, it is mainly a method for still or slow-flowing waters, the swifter currents of the ideal dace swim confounding one's best efforts to spot subtle bites. You can, of course, add Plasticine (or similar modelling clays) or lead wire to the end of the swingtip to counteract line drag on the current but, in practice, I have found that this can reduce the sensitivity of the method dramatically relative to the simple quivertip.

The traditional dough or silver paper bobbin, attached to a loop of slack reel line slung between two rod rings, suffers the same fate as the 'monkey climber'. It is a method best suited to registration of slower bites, and the requirement for line to run through the rod rings can offer too much resistance for dace. The same consideration applies too to swing indicators that attach to the butt of the rod.

Also, carp tactics are out! Obvious, I know, but I recall a winter in the late 1980s on the Hampshire Avon when a fellow was fishing a known dace swim with 'rod pod', paired electronic bite indicators and 'monkey climber' indicators. He grew more frustrated all day at the number of quick bites he was missing mounted inexorably, and was adamant that the problem was with the 'finicky' fish and not his approach as it worked OK for carp and tench! The method failed, however, on two of the key criteria noted above. 'Monkey climbers' are just too slow a method of bite detection for the sprightly dace, and the rig overall offered just too great a resistance for such delicate fish.

Ledgering offers many options for presenting appropriate baits to hungry dace when they are feeding, or can be lured to feed, on the bed of the river. But just remember that ledgering is not 'the lazy man's method' that it was once considered; you have to be alert and adaptive at all times to maximise the benefits it can bring.

Lessons from those estuarine dace

In the chapter *Bait*, I illustrated how bait choice and the style of feeding may need to change over a quite short time by describing a period of just a couple of hours catching dace on the tidal River Exe in Devon. I will not repeat the story here, but I will reiterate that the key lesson was an adaptation of waggler, Avon and ledger techniques and feeding regimes to stay in touch with dace and other fish as they moved about in the strong and often chaotic currents of the rising and falling river.

There is no one single approach that is best, whether in perpetuity, over a tidal cycle or indeed within any quarter-hour period. Let the river and the response of the fish you seek teach you about adapting techniques seamlessly to maintain your contact with a feeding dace shoal.

Dace on the fly and lure

We have noted previously the similar adaptations of the dace and the trout. It should therefore be no surprise that both species take flies and their aquatic larvae freely, adapted as they are to picking out drifting food items in faster flows. In fact, for many authors, taking dace on the fly is the best way to savour their qualities. As Bernard Venables, no less, says of dace in his inimitable *Mr Crabtree Goes Fishing*,

> *"It is not until they are fished for with fly tackle that they can really be regarded as sporting fish. And then indeed they can give very pretty sport."*

The great Pennell – the late nineteenth century angling innovator and author Henry Cholmondeley-Pennell who is responsible for, amongst other things, the dual-hooked 'Pennell rig' for worming and the Black Pennell fly – commended fly fishing for dace, noting that they…

> *"…make a gallant fight when hooked."*

William J. Howes, in his 1959 *Fly-fishing for Coarse Fish* was no less enthusiastic about fly-fishing for dace, noting that,

> *"This swift moving little fish is a worthy quarry for the angler fishing with fly, for the dace is a small but extremely game fish."*

Furthermore, Geoffrey Bucknall says in his 1968 *Fly-fishing Tactics on Rivers*,

> *"It would be foolish to ignore the dace, and I introduce this fish into my book as a token of respect for the pleasant days I have passed in its pursuit."*

That the fly is a killing method for dace, and big dace too, is evidenced by many writers. The late great angler and angling author Hugh Tempest Sheringham famously took five dace of over a pound in a single season, 1906, the largest weighing 1lb 2½oz. Fantastic fishing by any standards, and all of them were caught not just on the fly but on one particular pattern: a Brunton's Fancy (invented by Dr John Brunton).

Indeed, in their delightful and humorous 1925 book *Fishing: Its Cause, Treatment and Cure*, Sheringham and G.E. Studdy state that the dace,

> "Is always recommended as the fish on which the young fly-fisher
> shall try his practice hand. This is because it is the most difficult of
> all fish to hook on a fly."

As for the regular coarse angling methods, there is no special tackle requirement when presenting the fly to dace. Almost any regular river trout rod will do although tackle no heavier than a five weight, and ideally as fine as a three weight, will add to the day's pleasure and the subtlety of presentation. There is no need for a sinking line. Dace are keen on the dry fly, but rarely will you need to present a wet fly deep enough to need anything other than a sinking leader at the end of your regular floating line. The fly itself need not be anything out of the regular run of the mill. As Bernard Venables again says in *Mr Crabtree Goes Fishing*,

> "…almost any small fly will do – black gnat, olive dun, red quill,
> 'coch-y-bundhu' – but it must be small…""

Most angling authors who touch upon fly fishing for dace, myself included, agree on this point about dace being less than picky on choice of fly. And then each of them provides us with a list of preferred flies despite their assurance that our choice matters less than we might think! Some angling authors also suggest 'spicing up' a standard fly by the attachment of a little bait on the bend of the hook. For example, in *The Technique of Freshwater Fishing and Tackle Tinkering* (1971), W.E. Davies recommends that,

> "A very good fly is the Red Spinner and in the evening the addition
> of a maggot on the bend of the hook can be very productive."

However, Geoffrey Bucknall notes a specific preference in his 1968 *Fly-fishing Tactics on Rivers*,

> *"Like the rudd, the dace is addicted to the smuts, midges and gnats. It also feeds heavily on the Caenis, the so-called 'Angler's Curse'."*

Another point of general agreement is the need for a rapid strike. As Geoffrey Bucknall puts it in his 1968 *Fly-fishing Tactics on Rivers*,

> *"THE DACE is a mercurial fish, both in its silvery appearance as well as its quicksilver dash to the fly. The traditional pause before sending home the hook into the lip of a trout or chub must be ignored when you are deliberately fishing for dace....*
>
> *"Never neglect the mercurial dace. It's a useful test for your sluggish reactions, better than all of those fairground machines."*

The dry fly

In *Mr Crabtree Goes Fishing*, Bernard Venables famously chronicles the exploits of Mr Crabtree and his son, Peter, as they fish with the dry fly for dace in autumn. He rightly highlights a fantastic and mobile method for taking dace that works from spring through to summer, and even sometimes right through into the winter too. On the day before I wrote this paragraph, I had been watching a shoal of dace feeding off the surface during a morning of bitter frost!

For H.T. Sheringham, the allure of presenting a fly for the dace of the suburban River Thames in Edwardian England was great. As already mentioned in the Introduction to Part II of this book, he wrote in his 1910 book *An Open Creel* that,

> *"The angler might travel very much farther and fare very much worse. That is my thought every time I visit Isleworth fly-rod in hand..."*

Arthur P Bell, in his 1930 *Fresh-water Fishing for the Beginner*, notes of fly fishing for dace that,

> "Dace provide splendid sport for the fly fisherman, and can often be seen dashing along the surface, rising here and there on their way. The fly used should be a small one fished dry (i.e., floating on the surface), and the angler should endeavour to place it on the surface just ahead of a shoal. If a fish sees it he will rise with such rapidity that the angler will find it very hard to hook him. However, with a good deal of practice some excellent bags of dace can be taken in this sporting way. These fish are not frightfully particular as to the pattern of fly, but the writer has done well with a small hackle "Wickham's Fancy" and a tiny winged "Gold-ribbed hare's ear". It might be said that, although considerably easier to attract than the trout, the dace is harder to hook."

John Bailey and Roger Miller describe the lack of discrimination of types of dry fly taken by dace in their 1990 book *Chub and Dace*,

> "We have not found dace to be over-critical of the fly patterns and any small (say, size 18) black, blue or white pattern will attract them. There does not seem to be quite the need to match the hatches as there is with trout or even grayling, but good presentation, as in all dace fishing, is vitally important. If the fly is presented over the fish with the least amount of drag upon it, it will be refused."

E. Marshall-Hardy describes the catholic tastes of dace in his 1942 *Coarse Fish*, proceeding then to recommend the Black Spider, Red and Yellow Tag, Black Gnat, Wickham's Fancy and Black Palmer (with silver twist on body). Likewise, in the 1958 *Dace: How to Catch Them*, William J. Howes suggests that any dry fly will do, though commending the Black Gnat, Dark Olive Quill, Wickham's Fancy, Red Tag, Coachman, Coch-y-Bonddu, Greenwell's Glory, Zulu, Alder and Olive Dun, and reiterating a substantially similar list in his 1959 *Fly-fishing for Coarse Fish*.

I concur with all of these authors in their observation that dace are less fussy about choice of dry fly than one might have become accustomed in pursuing trout, and I would add to this list my two favourite dry flies: the Grannom Sedge and the Heron Grey.

The authors tatty tying of the Grannom proves deadly for hungry dace!

The wet fly

The same comments about the catholic taste of dace in taking flies extend below the surface. Wet flies are offered at varying depths depending upon weight of fly, speed of retrieve, time allowed for the fly to sink and the extent of greasing of the leader. Geoffrey Bucknall suggests in his 1968 *Fly-fishing Tactics on Rivers* that,

> *"When searching for dace in fast runs or stickles, it may be necessary to use a weighted nymph which will reach its working depth before it is swept past the fish."*

Howes and other authors offer no recommendations for favourite wet flies. So here I will suggest two of my own personal, proven favourites.

The first of these is a fly variously known as the 'Grasshopper Nymph' and a host of other names, comprising little more than buff wool wrapped from eye to bend over copper wire, with the bright metal tying off the wool above the bend of the hook.

This is best presented upstream 'nymphing' style, i.e. sinking or on a slight ascending retrieve in front of a feeding dace, though it also works admirably fished downstream.

The simple grasshopper nymph, little more than twists of wool and copper, is deadly for dace, grayling and trout.

The second is Richard Walker's versatile Crawler pattern. In its original green wool and brown silk tying with leaded body and pheasant 'back' and 'legs', it most closely resembles a damsel fly larva. However, I tie it in a wide range of colours and sizes, sometimes with a small piece of buoyant foam replacing the lead, to imitate anything from roach fry through to drowned black houseflies. It is a killer of a fly for virtually any species that swims, with dace showing a marked affinity for a 'roach fry' tying of grey/silver wool body, red wool 'tail', 'back' and 'fins', finished with translucent silk. You can have fun with this fly, tying it to match virtually anything that swims!

Crawler patterns tied in different colours and sizes are deadly for most fish.

Though it may be heresy to the fly-fishing purist, as we have discussed above some authors extol the virtues of baited flies. Typically, this is a little worm or maggot on the bend of the hook, to incite a firm take from furtive dace, perch, mullet and other fishes. The method works as well for the wet fly as for the dry, and may just make the difference on a day when the dace are in a fickle mood. In practice, however, I find that the bait is usually flicked off or eviscerated almost instantly it is cast, and so don't use this approach any more.

In passing, I should also note that there is a wet fly named after the dace. This is, however, the American Black Nose Dace fly, tied to imitate the black-nosed dace (which is in the carp/minnow family but is not a true 'dace' as we know them in Europe). They are usually tied large, on size 2 or 4 hooks, to tempt trout, panfish and bass.

The 'damp fly'

OK, I admit, there is no such thing as a 'damp fly'! However, we have to learn to innovate if we are to say one step ahead of the fish we seek. Tradition has it that we offer dry flies at the surface with no drag, whilst beneath the surface we offer the equally drag-free nymph or the slowly-retrieved wet fly. But sometimes the dace want something else. One such innovation was stumbled upon by H.T. Sheringham, in pursuit of dace from the tidal Thames,

> "Then they ceased to come up to it at all, either wet or dry, until I accidentally got a rise in recovering the fly as it floated. This led to experiments, and I found that, by letting the fly fall dry and then dragging it for a few inches along the surface, I got plenty of rises, and pretty bold ones too. The fish came at it before it had gone six inches or not at all, and for an hour I had quite a brisk bit of sport, so much so that on reaching the ferry I did not hesitate to estimate the number of fish kept as three dozen."

The topic of presenting a simulated drowned fly is not dissimilar to the 'spent fly' discussed by William J. Howes in *Fly-fishing for Coarse Fish*, which may comprise a greased wet fly or a dampened dry fly.

The use of controllers for fly presentation

Some authors recommend the use of controllers with the natural fly. These are small floats, or floating materials, that aid casting but are not intended for bite indication. I do not recommend them, except in the instance of presenting live floating insects – bluebottles, grasshoppers, etc. – to slightly extend your 'reach' when dapping or casting the free-line. (We have covered this already in the prior chapter *Free-line, float and ledger*.) Bubble floats, 'twisted twigs' and other methods will serve you well if you decide this method is for you.

An example of a proprietary controller for floating baits and flies.

Lures and fishy baits

What on earth is a section on predator fishing doing in a book on dace? Well, because, as addressed in *Part I* of this book, dace can be predatory, within a generally omnivorous diet. In practice, the difference between a big invertebrate and a small fry is not much; both are meaty and mobile snacks that a hungry fish of almost any species will seize if available!

Geoffrey Bucknall asserts in his 1968 *Fly-fishing Tactics on Rivers* that,

> *"...it's not generally realised that the dace is inclined to be somewhat predatory by nature, and in common with all predators, it is attracted by flash."*

Dace are attracted to flashy wet flies. The pattern on the right is 'Everard's Monstrosity' tied with lead wire, red wood and a dab of his daughter's glitter glue... and it catches dace!

Lure fishing

In discussing wet fly fishing for dace, I have addressed the fact that fish-like lures are the best for dace. Other authors too have questioned whether we are overlooking a potent method for selecting big dace. This chapter may just challenge some assumptions.

Many is the angler, myself included, who has caught dace and other unexpected 'non-predatory' coarse fish on small lure; sometimes even on big ones too! For example, one edition of Richard Walker's famous book *Stillwater Angling* (first published in 1953), contains an illustration of some very large roach caught on lightweight bar-spoons armed with small trebles set well to the rear and decorated with feathers.

William J Howes recalls in his 1958 book *Dace: How to Catch Them*, that,

> *"I well remember the occasion while spinning for perch with a small 'Vibro' lure when I hooked a fish which, at first sight, I thought to be a small chub, but which subsequently proved to be a fairly large dace. This fish was cleanly hooked in the mouth, and I have no doubt that it deliberately took the spinner."*

Mike Ladle and Harry Casey, in their 1988 book *Lure Fishing: A New Approach to Spinning*, throw down the gauntlet by saying that,

> *"An angler with initiative, patience and access to waters where shoaling roach or other fish of the carp family grow to a good size, could possibly produce spectacular catches by developing his own mini, lightweight, long-shanked worm or maggot/baited bar-spoons. The technique will probably involve a longish rod for lure control, lines of 3-6 pounds B.S. on a fixed spool reel and a very slow retrieve. The approach will be suck-it-and-see. This seems, to us, to be one of the most exciting challenges which remain in angling, for while we have personally caught such unlikely species as dace, rudd and bream on small, unbaited bar-spoons, Heaven knows what we might have caught if we had had the foresight to add bait to the hooks. Here indeed, is scope for research."*

A fly spoon, once a common piece of tackle but rarely seen today, may be a solution when contemplating spinning for the small-mouthed dace. The bend of the hook may be either baited or left without bait. For the most subtle presentation, David Carl Forbes suggests in his 1966 book *Small Stream Fishing* that the best presentation of a small lure is below a float, beneath which it can be worked sink-and-draw style through the different levels of the water. I have tried this method successfully in the United States for flounders and speckled trout (a spiny-finned estuarine fish not related to our trout at all) and know that it works. However, I have never yet tried it yet for dace in British waters!

Perhaps the future of specimen dace angling? Or not??

No one that I know of has seriously taken up the challenge of the deliberate capture of big dace on lures by design. Perhaps we are missing a trick? After all, perhaps the biggest surprise of all is that we are surprised at just how predatory omnivorous fish are in the wild! Dace in particular are adapted to intercept swallowable prey and vegetable matter from faster flows, and that includes larger insects and smaller fish of the same size. Which brings us on to fish baits.

Live and dead baits?

Peter Wheat is not alone in thinking about the predatory habits of dace when he relates in his 1975 book *Catch More Dace* the not uncommon observation that large dace are sometimes caught full of, indeed regurgitating, minnows. He also notes that he and colleagues have sometimes incidentally caught big dace on live and dead minnow baits. A big dace has a significant body mass to maintain, so a substantial, rich food item has energetic advantages over working hard to pick up many less energy-dense alternatives. Are small live or dead fish baits techniques for singling out really large dace, or indeed other cyprinids, which we have thus far overlooked? I, for one, think that this may be the case.

Fish care

In my *The Complete Book of the Roach*, I devoted a very long chapter on fish care in which I rolled in various comments on handling, retaining, weighing, photographing, unhooking, etc. I thought this was novel but important, highlighting the central importance of fish care in all we do. However, I have since found, to my great surprise and pleasure, that Peter Wheat also devoted a little over two pages of text to the final chapter *Care of the Catch*, in his 1975 book *Catch More Dace*. I thoroughly approve of this!

So it is with no apology that I will make some extended comments here about caring for what we catch, though not replicating all the details in my previous book. Although I focus primarily upon those matters in which dace are most likely to suffer inadvertent harm at our hands, fish care should shape *everything* that we do as caring anglers; for the fish themselves, the wellbeing of the fishery, the reputation of angling, and for our own good conscience and karma!

Group shots like this are safe enough only if the net is wet, and grass is damp and the day is cool enough not to stress the fish.

It can go without further comment that kind hooks without massive barbs will be the norm, with micro-barbed or barbless hooks favoured, and that your baits are carefully prepared to prevent seeds swelling within the fish or harmful additives putting them at risk. If, like me, you are more accustomed to larger hooks for most of your fishing and have found a pattern that slips easily from the mouths of larger fish, beware of automatically assuming that the same pattern will be as kind to the mouth of a fish at just one or two sizes smaller. I have found it necessary to experiment with the kindest hooks; if you exert more than the merest pressure to slip the hook out then you risk unacceptable damage to the mouth of the fish. Also, ensure that you will play your dace gently to the net. It is from this point that we will pick up our main fish care considerations.

A landing net must be used on larger fish to avert the risk of damage to the mouth, or other organs around the mouth for a more deeply-hooked fish. This net must be of knotless mesh (a legal requirement in England and Wales) and the handle should be long enough to reach down from high banks and to avert the risk of snaring hooked dace on bank-side vegetation.

When lifting the netted fish from the water, there are yet more factors to consider. The first of these is to lift the net and not drag it up a bank that may have sharp thorns or rocks which can damage the fish. The second is to ensure that the fish are adequately supported and certainly never dropped. They are adapted to life immersed in a buoyant medium, for which a strong skeleton to bear their weight in air is not required, so inadequate care in handling can do serious harm. Likewise, try to avoid stressing the fish, as they are used to sweeping their flanks against the viscous medium of water; thrashing around in unyielding thin air can stress the muscles and skeleton, quite apart from causing the fish to harm themselves against hard objects on the bank.

We have also to recall that light is quickly attenuated in water, and that even a dull day on land is massively brilliant to an aquatic animal that lacks eyelids. Protecting fish from the heat and glare of full sunlight is essential, and shielding them from the brightest light with your body or else with a covering of wet mesh is important at all other times. Bear in mind too that the medium of water buffers the dace from extremes of temperature generally within a narrow 'window' of roughly 4°C to 18°C across the natural range of the dace. A frosty, snowy or hot day on land can exceed these limits significantly, so fish must be protected accordingly. Never, ever put them down on hot (and dry) banks or on frosty or snow-covered surfaces, even for a moment, and also bear in mind that fins are vulnerable to rapid frostbite in cold air and to drying out in warmer conditions. If necessary, rest the fish on freshly-wetted netting on the bank but, better still, put them back in the water.

It is when unhooking dace that the inexperienced can cause inadvertent harm. This may be by holding the fish in dry hands, which is an absolute 'no-no' as this strips the protective mucus from the surface of the fish leaving it vulnerable to parasitic attack. Always wet your hands before handing fish. It is also vitally important to check that you don't grip the fish too tight. There is no need for any more than a firm but gentle pressure to steady the fish, and to stop it flicking out of your grip to hurt itself should it fall.

It is also absolutely essential for an angler to carry a disgorger (ideally more than one) or a pair of artery forceps to unhook fish when the hook can not simply be slipped from the mouth. A great piece of advice offered to me, and which I have written before and shamelessly repeat here, is to carry three disgorgers: one for your own use, one as a spare, and one to give away to any other angler you discover who does not own one. If I ruled the world, anglers would not be allowed to fish without a disgorger about their person!

If you need to keep fish, for match fishing or specimen purpose, a large pike tube or keep net made of knotless netting will suffice. Buckets are too small and the dace can too easily deplete the oxygen in them or, more likely, jump out. Likewise, keep sacks are fine for big, robust species but will tend to collapse onto dace and suffocate them. The keep net should be staked either end so that your dace are not pinned by river currents against the flat end of the net. The principle of lifting, not dragging, the net up the bank is essential to protect your fish from abrasion.

When weighting and photographing my prize, I tend to set the camera on the monopod (or set it up for the witness when one is needed) and zero the scales on a wet weight sling before removing the dace from the water. Then, the weighing and photos can be done in one smooth movement without any more delay to set things up, leaving the dace vulnerable to thrashing against hard objects, drying out, cold or heat. Furthermore, I check the front of my clothing for zips and other hard, potentially damaging objects, and I also take my watch off as the buckle can harm the fish as well as interfere with the 'naturalness' of the shot. Keep the fish out of the water for as short a time as possible, as the thin fins are quick to suffer frostbite in the cold or to dry out in the warm.

A further tip about photographing dace is to try to do so without flash photography whenever possible as the brilliance of the fish against a drab background tends to 'bleach out' all detail. And, if you need to have the fish formally identified from the photos, you have to retain as much detail of the scales along the lateral line, the dorsal and anal fins extended to enable counting of the spines and rays, and close-ups of the head and mouth. For a specimen shot, you may also want to place the fish against a reference object – a ruler, a lens cap, or similar – so that the length can be verified later.

Return the fish to the water as quickly as possible, holding upright any fish that does not dart off immediately. With a little patience, they will generally recover promptly and swim off strongly once re-orientated and re-oxygenated. It is essential that you do this as fish, bird and other predators are always ready to take a vulnerable dace. If you need to keep your dace on the bank for a longer photographic session, periodically 'freshen up' the fish in a net to keep them healthy.

Do fish feel pain and suffer distress? The answer, based on scientific research that I have reviewed at length in my 2006 *The Complete Book of the Roach*, is that fish possess dense chemical sense organs in the mouth area, though those associated with physical sensations are less dense enabling them to tackle their sometimes thorny, biting and armed prey with ease. Furthermore, 'pain' is a subjective sensation for which fish lack the necessary brain structure for conscious thought processing. They will, however, respond in a programmed way to certain stimuli, such as struggling against a pressure such as a tight fishing line, and this is what we experience as the 'fight'. However, slacken the line and release the pressure and the fish will then cease to respond, having no 'pain' against which to react. Fish then lack the nervous and brain 'wiring' to perceive pain in quite the way that mammals do.

But this does not leave the angler 'off the hook' as we can stress fish by careless treatment, which makes them vulnerable to their myriad parasites and predators, so we had better take the best possible care of them at all times: in the water, on the fight, on the bank, and when returning them.

We need to do everything in our powers to minimise harm in any form to our fish. If we are caring anglers, respecting the river bank and doing our bit to combat would-be polluters or promote river protection or restoration, our net impact on the wellbeing of fish stocks should not just be neutral but rather be significantly beneficial. That is something about which you may feel justifiable pride.

Management of a dace fishery

Dace are the quintessential *Prince of the Stream*; perhaps even the poor man's brown trout. They thrive where flows are fresh, with good diversity of habitat from gravel shallows to deeper glides supporting the needs of their various life stages throughout the year. This kind of diverse habitat also provides the wide range of food items that sustain dace. Clean water, adequate currents, a complexity of flow patterns and a balanced stream ecosystem make for vibrant dace populations.

A legacy of human mismanagement

In so many ways, human activities erode each of these characteristics. Many have done so for millennia in our small, densely-populated isles, with smaller rivers often the most vulnerable.

Pollution is a persistent and pernicious issue. It may stem from point sources such as effluent from sewage works or industrial plants, or more worryingly today from myriad diffuse sources including contaminated run-off from agriculture, highways and from urban and industrial areas. All such contamination delivers a dirty influx of suspended and dissolved matter deleterious to aquatic life. Suspended sediment with associated chemical pollutants enters our rivers directly from engineering works and trampling of stream edges by livestock, as well as indirectly through development of the built environment and from agricultural land use.

These chemical and physical effects are exacerbated by the loss of flow energy to flush sediment through river systems, clean out gravels and generate physical habitat structure. These influences therefore also degrade riverine habitat quality and diversity. And then we abstract huge quantities of water from both surface waters and the underground strata essential for replenishing streams. We do this for the quite valid purposes of supporting our own domestic, industrial and agricultural uses.

However, so great is the rate of abstraction that it commonly serves to reduce the dilution of pollutants, to decrease the habitat-maintaining and gravel-cleaning processes in flowing waters, and generally to exacerbate wider changes in river ecosystems that are disadvantageous to dace, trout and many other native fishes.

Add to this the various man-made obstructions to the movement of fish, not only up and down rivers but also across them from the river channel into impoverished, over-managed complex vegetation at stream edges and adjacent wetland habitat. It is hardly a surprise then that dace are one of many species perceived to be in decline due to continuing human development.

River management for dace

Let's face it, the above sub-title is hopelessly optimistic! No-one is going to manage a fishery just for the benefit of dace. However, think of dace as an indicator of healthy flows, good quality water and habitat, and diverse invertebrate food, and it quickly becomes apparent that management for dace would be a wise move for the benefit of the whole fishery ecosystem, of wide benefit also to self-sustaining populations of trout and coarse fishes. Dace are, in so many ways, a sensitive barometer of aquatic quality as well as being a fish that bites freely in all conditions much to the enjoyment of virtually all anglers.

Putting our ecological understanding of the fish itself at the forefront of our minds helps us think through optimal fishery management.

Righting the wrongs

So many fishery management decisions seek to address problems from the wrong end. How often does one hear calls for restocking and/or predator management? If there are fundamental problems with a fishery which remain unaddressed, stocked fish will fail either to prosper or to breed, and the wisdom of such an investment will be exposed in the longer term. We will discuss predators a little later in this chapter, but the same principle also applies. Predators are an essential part of the balance of natural ecosystems, so if the fishery can not support a head of predators then there is usually a more fundamental problem with the vitality of the fodder fish rather than with excess predatory species. More often than not, the call for predator management has little to do with any objective evaluation of predator versus prey populations, but is rather a knee-jerk reaction to poor perceived fishing which may have entirely different causes. Better then to focus on the basic parameters of environmental quality. If these are correct then nature will ensure thriving and sustainable fish populations.

Water quality is one of the fundamental parameters determining the health of a fishery. It varies naturally, shaped largely by the geology of the catchment from which rivers run, and the fish stocks naturally present will be those best adapted to local variations in quality. However, it is the activities of man that concern us most here, particularly pollution from point and diffuse sources discussed above. If you suspect a pollution incident, act immediately by reporting it to the relevant regulatory authority. If you suspect other continuous lower-grade contamination of your water, such as more diffuse pollution and sediment impacts from insensitive upstream farming or development of urban areas or transport infrastructure, report that too. Identifying sources and determining appropriate action is a job for experts, but making those experts aware is very much a job for all of us.

Likewise, rivers vary naturally in size and flow rate. However, mankind has a hand in modifying rates of river flow, and in many ways. We over-abstract water for human uses from surface and underground sources, which reduces river flows. And we drain land for agriculture and urban and industrial development, such that water no longer infiltrates into the ground freely to be subsequently released into rivers through a buffered 'sponge effect'. Rather, in an impermeable or over-drained environment, rainfall rushes off the land bearing a load of pollutants in a 'boom and bust' of flash flooding interspersed with starved flows. Such extremes of flow also need your attention. Solutions are often highly complex, entailing restoration of crucial wetland habitats across whole landscapes, but planning for such restoration can only start with awareness and a call for action.

All of this affects the habitat structure of rivers, exacerbated too by unsympathetic direct river management, often for flood control purposes, that degrades the ecological value of our flowing waters. Fish need diverse habitat features and flow regimes throughout the year and throughout life histories, as do the organisms that they feed upon. We therefore have to do all we can to stop destructive river management, including overzealous 'swim improvements'. Leaving wild reaches is almost invariably a good thing, providing a diversity of habitat for the various life stages of different fish species at different times of the day and season, building supplies of their food, and providing refuges for other wildlife. Diversification of river habitat benefits the entire ecosystem, the aesthetics of the river and its angling diversity and challenges.

Leaving unmanaged river stretches adds to the diversity, mystery and enjoyment of rivers.

And the more we can avoid the introduction of non-native species, the better will be the health of our fishery. Some such as the American signal crayfish (and other non-native crayfish species), invasive plants such as the New Zealand swamp stonecrop, and various alien fish species can change ecosystem dynamics, carry foreign diseases and destabilise habitat structure. Other native species when introduced out of their natural range, even seemingly desirable introductions such as barbel in rivers where they do not naturally occur, can also harm rivers by disrupting their locally-adapted ecosystems.

Stockings of even native fish species from other waters can carry diseases that are not present in your water. Introduced plant species such as Japanese knotweed, giant hogweed, Himalayan balsam and so forth, can swamp the native plant species upon which ecosystems depend, expose river banks to erosion as they die back, as well as potentially produce substances toxic to humans. The best policy is management to retain or restore natural processes sustaining native organisms, and the careful exclusion of any introductions of either alien or non-local organisms.

Like many non-native species, the signal crayfish can carry disease, damage bank and habitat structure, prey upon vulnerable native species of plants and animals, compete with them for food, and generally perturb the delicate balance of river ecosystems.

Positive management

In the last years of the twentieth and the early years of the twenty-first century, bodies such as the *River Restoration Centre* (RRC), the *Wild Trout Trust* (WTT), and a range of local *River Trusts* have risen to the challenge of river enhancement. Often driven initially by salmonid fishery interests, but subsequently broadening out to reflect the interests in whole river ecosystems and their many beneficiaries, these bodies have championed restoration of habitat within rivers appropriate for the development of sustainable fish stocks, associated biological communities and regeneration of the rural economy supported by environmental and landscape quality.

Solutions to a range of the bigger-scale human impacts shaping river ecosystems, including factors influencing water quality, geomorphology ('earth-shaping') and hydrology, are complex, longer-term and sometimes poorly understood. They are matters for statutory control and long-term planning, pressure for which can most effectively be mounted by vocal and expert voluntary bodies. However, much can be done in the shorter term to redress at least some localised harm inflicted historically on river habitats, as well as to help river ecosystems function in spite of wider pressures on geomorphology, hydrology and, to a certain degree, restrictions brought about by water quality.

Practical help is available directly from these voluntary bodies. Some produce expert and accessibly-written manuals, such as the RRC's (1999) *The Manual of River Restoration Techniques* or the WTT's (2006) *The Wild Trout Survival Guide*. These practical river habitat improvement guides, and the organisations that wrote them, promote techniques such as stream narrowing to increase flows for feeding and spawning sites for trout and other fish, removal of obstructions to fish movement, clearing of stretches 'tunnelled' by tree overgrowth which limits in-stream macrophyte growth and invertebrate diversity, habitat improvement for the whole river ecosystem, re-meandering of straightened rivers, creation of backwaters for fry refuges, creation of wetland features, 'soft engineering' of river banks, reversing over-deepening of channels, sympathetic public and livestock access, and a host of other practical techniques.

For many of our rivers, the forces that created their structure operate only to a significantly diminished extent today. Catchment drainage, increased silt loads entering rivers, over-zealous historic channel straightening or dredging, unsympathetic re-profiling of river channels and banks, and disconnection of floodplains from river channels, not to mention a host of 'hard engineering' impacts on rivers such as sheet-piling of banks and weir creation, result in reduced habitat-maintaining energy from rivers flows. This is exacerbated by over-abstraction and climate change, which can rob rivers of their traditional winter scouring power. So, it is essential at times to narrow rivers, particularly those over-widened by engineered re-profiling, livestock poaching or reduced flows, to restore flow rates advantageous to fish and wildlife. With skill, life can be breathed back into a dull, lowland river that is seemingly doomed to a continued life of sluggish, muddy flows. The fish stocks will then respond as if by magic.

For the more adventurous fishery owner or manager who wants to make useful interventions to increase the diversity of flow, create local channel scour, introduce fry nurseries as well as ensure there are refuges for fish of all ages from spates and predators, it is worthwhile considering installing live willow deflectors. These structures are basically groynes comprising live willow trunks dug two-thirds of their length into the bank and projecting out perhaps one-third of the way across the river channel at roughly a 45° angle downstream to the flow. These are then staked with freshly-cut live willow to form a substantial structure, and the whole is woven with smaller supple live willow twigs. Unlike 'hard engineering' deflectors made of sheet metal or preserved timber, the willow grows to reinforce and increase habitat diversity with time, becoming a magnet for ducks and moorhens, kingfishers and invertebrates, different aquatic plant communities, and of course young fish of all species. Larger fish will position themselves near the accelerated current at the outer edge of the deflectors to intercept food brought to them in the current, and the localised gravel scour may be used as spawning habitat by some species. A live willow deflector can add real diversity, life and improved sport to a formerly over-straightened and over-dredged reach of river. You will need the consent of the relevant regulatory agencies, but the method is cheap, long-lasting due to its self-reinforcing nature, and highly effective if executed properly.

Newly-installed live willow deflectors designed by the author to add flow and wildlife diversity to a formerly over-managed reach of the Bristol Avon.

There are more modest, local modifications that can be made to small stream fisheries. David Carl Forbes mentions two in his 1966 book *Small Stream Fishing*: off-stream 'snail cultivation' and on-channel 'shrimp farming'. You may or may not want to go to these types of measures, and most will anyhow be impractical on bigger streams and rivers where the adequacy and diversity of habitat will see to most of the needs of dace and other fishes.

Many of the larger voluntary organisations noted above have also proven ingenious in connecting their work with regional economic regeneration, tapping into often significant grants to deliver regional economic stability or development on the back of the fishery and tourism value of a restored river. What is certain is that much can be done to counteract many of the forces that have degraded our rivers and their fisheries, for the good of trout, salmon, dace and other coarse fish, and the people who benefit from enhanced fisheries and local environments.

Planning a fishery

The important thing is that you know what you are seeking to maintain, what you hope to improve and why, and what you intend to eradicate or manage. It is also important that you share this knowledge, and ideally the initiatives to achieve it, with others. Some organisations, such as river trusts and environmental regulators, can help you directly. Others can recognise how their activities may either compromise your aspirations or else support them, resulting in a collaborative approach to fishery protection and enhancement that would not have been achievable without clear communication.

Too many fisheries are managed through *ad hoc* and short-term good intentions that are not seen through, or else abandoned in favour of tomorrow's 'good idea'. Goals are often thwarted simply because they have not been articulated clearly or understood by others. It is wisest always to look to the underpinning needs of the water and the longer-term projects that will contribute toward a richer fishery.

In general, there are no conflicts between fishery health and nature conservation objectives. After all, thriving fish stocks are a key indicator of healthy aquatic ecosystems, at least in the kind of river environments in which dace thrive. As anglers and fishery managers, we need to do more to promote this message of synergy and to advertise the wider conservation benefit and societal 'goods' that our river protection and enhancement activities deliver.

Central to fishery aspirations should be a written plan detailing exactly what is desired and why. This can also serve to coordinate the efforts of those sharing common goals, as well as providing a basis for achieving some kind of consensus with those who might otherwise act in conflict, for example canoeists or other navigation interests, farmers and other land users, or shooting rights.

By consulting with others and ensuring mutual understanding of each other's aspirations, sustainable management plans can be developed to maximise the value of everyone's energies and investments. This can be highly cost-effective, and also serve to flush out unforeseen opportunities such as the support of environmental regulators, or grant money from the EU or local authorities. This consensual approach will also help you plan any in-channel or bank top vegetation management, habitat enhancement, refuge area design, sensitive riparian land use, livestock or public access points, restrictions on angling seasons, access by boats and dogs, etc.

It is also wonderful to see goals achieved and, stepwise, to see progress towards realisation of the potential of a fishery and an ecosystem.

The perfect dace fishery

When mankind's negative influences have been curtailed or managed, where flows are strong and there is a diversity of habitat, current speed and natural food, dace will thrive. And where dace thrive, so will roach, trout and many other desirable fish species, not to mention kingfishers, dippers and other water birds reflective of a healthy river. Rivers and lakes, after all, support some of the UK's richest and best-loved biological resources. A good dace river is often something of great wildlife and amenity value; a place of beauty where all the pieces of nature's jigsaw are in place.

When we get it right, the populations of dace and other fish will rise from impoverished levels to realisation of an optimal 'carrying capacity'. As Nick Giles describes for trout (though the principles apply as exactly to dace and other fish) in his 2005 book *The Nature of Trout*,

> *"Carrying capacity (the number of trout a stream can support), varies with habitat quality, food availability, water flows and other climatic influences... This type of positive habitat management increases the 'carrying capacity' of the fishery and can be applied to various types of habitat needed by trout of differing sizes and ages. Where habitats are degraded, an understanding of this type of management is vital to the success of wild trout conservation."*

The factors limiting the achievement of theoretical carrying capacity can be exposed by 'Limiting Factor Analysis', identifying which of the parameters of water quality, river flows and levels, food provision and habitat diversity are limiting the potential fish population. Once the limiting factor is identified, corrective action can then be prioritised and the potential fulfilled.

In their 1990 book *Chub and Dace*, John Bailey and Roger Miller note of a perceived decline in dace populations and the reasons behind it that,

> *"There is no doubt, however, that their numbers are in decline for several reasons. Abstraction, pollution, livebait removal and chemical infiltration all play their deadly part. Equally, if not more dangerous, is the dredging and canalising of rivers that has taken place all over England since the 1960s. Dace need currents and streamy gravels very much indeed, but a straight, uniform drain of a river that runs like a train after winter rains does nothing for the fry and yearlings that find it virtually impossible to maintain their position without shelter.*

> *"In north Norfolk, the upper River Bure once held great dace stocks until the river was 'improved' in the 1960s. Thereafter, numbers fell steadily until in certain stretches, populations were virtually non-existent. This was the case at Abbot's Hall, until eight or nine years ago when a trout syndicate stepped in. Numerous groynes were built to scour the mud and clean the gravels. These groynes also gave shelter to small fish, and it was soon discovered that dace were beginning to return to the stretch for the first time since the Anglian Water Authority had stepped in. Today, the stretch is once again very rich in dace, and when electro-fished in the winter, dace are always found behind the groynes. This one physical improvement has radically altered the river, again making it suitable for dace, by creating the habitat which they need in order to survive."*

Bailey and Miller expose not only the general plight of our modern rivers, 'tamed' by over-management and excessive abstraction and inputs of agricultural run-off, silt and other forms of pollution, but also the 'silver lining' of recent restorative work with has the potential to return dace stock towards potential carrying capacity.

But let us be realistic that intense pressures remain on our vulnerable and much-loved rivers, and that dace may often serve as the 'miner's canary'. We must be ever vigilant and ready to speak out in protest to protect them. As John Bailey laments in his 1984 book *In Visible Waters*,

> *"…some years ago a feeder stream was dredged. Work took place in May, at the most vital time for all the life that tiny water fostered. It happened to be an important, hereditary dace spawning site and the gravelly pool that the main river fish used was swept totally away with that year's eggs — and many of the adult fish. At the time, I grieved for the frogs, toads, newts, waterbirds as well as the dace and though the former have recovered, the dace in that beat of river never have."*

> *"It is the dace's problem that there are few men who love them and their loss is mourned only by the few. They are not large, they cannot, because of their size, put up dramatic fights, they do not taste good and so have no commercial value and because of all this, their habitats are pushed back further and further."*

Dace may not be the most obvious target species for fishery management, but they are a barometer of all that goes to make a thriving fishery ecosystem in which fish of all species, diverse aquatic ecosystems and people all prosper.

Giant bags and whopping great dace

Dace are, let's face it, not the weightiest of fish that swim in British streams. However, even in a world seemingly addicted to 'bigness' – be that 'super-sized' junk food, mega-corporations displacing local trade and bespoke needs, or imported carp of bloated proportions – it would be wrong not to think of larger dace as anything less than true specimens.

Big bags of dace

Just before we dive into thoughts about notable specimen dace, we'll reserve a few words about big bags of dace. Despite their relatively light weight compared to some other river match fishing targets such as chub or bream, very large bags of dace can be assembled and particularly so when the fish are beginning to mass prior to spawning at the end of the coarse fishing season.

Inevitably, the best known and most accurately recorded of these fall to anglers fishing competitive matches.

One of the most spectacular bags of dace recorded in a fishing match was taken by Fred Buller, the famed specimen angler and angling historian who, in his early years, had distinguished himself as a match angler. On one occasion, Fred took a stunning and winning bag of 64lb, comprising no less than one-hundred-and-sixty-one dace.

William J Howes (*Dace: How to Catch Them*, 1958) notes what he believed then to be a record bag of dace.

> *"The Newport Angling Association's Groves Trophy Dace Match in 1956 provided a new record for a dace match on the River Usk. The four anglers at the head of the list had total weights as follows:*

Mr. J. Lennon,	1st.	42 lb. 15 oz. 8 dm.
Mr. D. Alexander,	2nd.	28 lb. 3 oz. 8 dm.
Mr. A. Friswell,	3rd.	17 lb. 10 oz.
Mr. J. Walker,	4th.	10 lb. 4 oz. 8 dm.

Out of the 44 competitors only fourteen weighed in fish, the total weight of which, however, was 127 lb. 7 oz. Indeed, a lot of dace!"

Nostalgia, as they say, ain't what it used to be. Dace are generally perceived to be declining as a result of various environmental forces. However, all is not necessarily 'doom and gloom', with notable catches of dace still possible. For example, dace catches during a match on the River Exe were sufficiently spectacular in September 2006 to warrant a banner headline in the angling weekly *Angling Times* (3rd October edition). The paper recorded that the River Exe produced its best result in 50 years with more than 130lb of dace shared between 20 rods in a four-and-a-half hour match, topped by a bag of 33lb 8oz of dace taken by local rod Roly Palmer using classic 'wag and mag' tactics. This winning weight was backed up by bags of dace of 24lb 8oz and 22lb 8oz, a terrific aggregate weight of dace entirely locking out the podium!

To trump this on Wednesday 8th November 2006, former England International match angler Dave Harrell caught a staggering 114lb 11oz of dace in a five-hour match at Peg No.96 on the Belmont section of the River Wye near Hereford, a peg normally noted for chub. Dave rated this catch as one of the best catches of his life, taking the majority of the fish using a 4x No.4 shot stick float and using eight kilogrammes of groundbait in additional to a gallon of hemp and casters. Dave told me of his catch that,

"In the run up to the first real frosts of the year, the dace move from the shallower water upstream of Hereford into the deeper water between the bridges in the town centre. Peg 96 is known for giving

*good weights of chub and cracking nets of dace from time to time.
In fact the peg had given most of the big nets of dace in the week
before the festival.*

*"Previously, myself and several other anglers had landed 60lb nets
of dace in matches, and I felt that 80lbs would be the most it was
possible to catch. Some of the regular locals thought a 'ton' might
be on the cards, but those of us who had landed 60+ thought that
was optimistic.*

*"I waded out into the river and stood up to fish a 7 metre whip,
feeding groundbait every cast and fishing double maggot on the
hook. It soon became clear that I was on for a good day, and
managed to feed the fish in closer, so that I could fish at 6 metres
and catch even quicker. Very rarely do you get that perfect
combination of a good angler on a good peg in good conditions,
but that was one of those days. At the end of the match, I thought
I had over 80lbs, but it wasn't until I tried to lift the net out that I
realised I must have over the ton. It was fantastic to catch those fish
and 114lbs of dace is something very special."*

Well done Dave on what is generally believed to be a match record for dace, and
thanks for the quote!

Up to half a pound

Dace reach a peak age of some ten or eleven years, a considerable age for such
a relatively small species, though the vast majority of fish fall to predation or
disease well before this. You may recall from our consideration of the
reproduction and growth of dace in *Part I* of this book that about half of the annual
production by dace in a stretch of river may be accounted for by fish of under one
year old, and that the huge mortality rate amongst younger fish slowly declines
as they age to result in a 'pyramid' of numbers of dace of different ages topped

by a scarcity of older and therefore bigger fish. Therefore, fish that weight just a few ounces constitute the bulk of a dace population, and a half-pound is not an unreasonable upper size limit in many waters.

This means that the 'small' dace you may be catching on a regular basis really are scarce beasts, the venerable products of a seemingly impossible struggle over many years against predators, diseases and environmental extremes. It is important to appreciate and value every one of them.

Half to one pound

We are talking specimens here! A dace that has grown to such proportions has done well and, in spite of their relatively small stature as measured against a chub or barbel, look surprisingly big. Only the exceptional few, most often in rivers of a distinct character or else where populations and competition are low, ever get to exceed half-a-pound. Dace beyond this weight are exceptional fish, silvery and beautiful.

William J Howes states quite accurately in his 1958 book *Dace: How to Catch Them*, that,

> "On most waters even a half-pound dace can be considered well worth noting in the diary."

John Bailey and Roger Miller, in the *Days with Dace* chapter of their 1990 book *Chub and Dace*, make a distinction about dace weighing more than ten ounces,

> "Bigger fish, however, the 'doubles', present a true specialist challenge."

For many specialist anglers, twelve ounces marks the distinction between dace that are specimens rather than merely being 'big'. As Peter Wheat puts it in his 1975 book *Catch More Dace*,

"A dace of 12oz from any water, no matter how high-class, is specimen size and equivalent in stature to a 2lb roach. Having said that, I am quite sure that many readers will disagree with this rating, suggesting in turn 1lb as minimum for a 'glass-caser'."

Peter goes on to make a well-reasoned argument that a 2lb roach weights 51.61% of the (then) British Record of 3lb 14 oz, whereas a 1lb dace is 66.66% of the largest authenticated (though not in the eyes of the British Record (Rod Caught) Fish Committee) dace of 1lb 8oz. Whilst not arguing with the conclusion, I would however note that a 12oz dace is 56.80% of the (current) British Record fish of 1lb 5oz 2dr.

Whatever the statistical details, a big fat dace is a wonderful creature of platinum flank and sprightly fight. These big dace are often referred to by the affectionate nick-name 'herrings', because of their broad, silvery appearance and (for female fish at least) the soft feel of their pre-spawning flanks.

Pound-plus dace

A pound-plus dace is a rare beast indeed, and a beauty to behold too! Along with the classic two-pound roach, such a fish is generally considered to be 'the fish of a lifetime' for the lucky captor. Emphasising their rarity, E. Marshall-Hardy says in his book *Coarse Fish*, that,

"A pound Dace is a rare glass-case specimen, the like of which does not fall once in a lifetime to the rod of most anglers…

"If you catch a pound Dace, have it "set up"; it is more than probable that it will be the first and last."

Whilst I agree generally with Marshall-Hardy, I'd obviously recommend instead that you take a lot of decent photos and put the fish back alive! However, I find myself nodding vigorously in agreement with John Bailey and Roger Miller when, in the *Days with Dace* chapter of their 1990 book *Chub and Dace*, they note of dace beyond the magical one-pound barrier that,

> *"The true pounder is a target probably as difficult as a chub six times that weight."*

To attain a weight of 1lb, a dace must not only find itself in ideal conditions but must also survive in the face of myriad daily threats for at least seven and more probably eight years, based on scale readings from fish of that calibre. That is a very long time for a 'bite-sized chunk' like a dace!

William J. Howes too chimes in about dace above and below the pound mark in his 1959 *Fly-fishing for Coarse Fish*,

> *"Dace weighing up to ½ lb. are common enough, but a 14 or 15 oz. dace may be considered a good fish, and any dace over a pound exceptional."*

In concluding about pound-plus dace, I would add that, despite many specialists, myself included, catching some of our biggest dace by design, I agree wholeheartedly with Peter Wheat's analysis (in *Catch More Dace*) that,

> *"The majority of 1lb dace captures are the result of sheer luck rather than planned design."*

The take-home message is that, though a pound-plus dace may look puny next to a run-of-the-mill barbel or chub, do appreciate what a rare beast it really is!

The 'Magic Double'

It was the late and very great Richard Walker who coined the phrase 'The Magic Double'. Just as a two-pound roach is still considered the 'fish of a lifetime', so too is a pound-plus dace exceptional. For Walker, the 'Magic Double' was the capture of a two-pound roach and a one-pound dace from the same session. This is as probable as getting hit by lightening twice in succession, albeit that one is left with a huge grin rather than life-threatening burns!

I have done the 'Magic Double' six times myself as I write, inevitably from rivers including both the Hampshire Avon and the Bristol Avon. Fantastic!

The 'Magic Triple'

There is only one recorded instance of the 'triple lightening strike' event of the 'Magic Triple', a term that I coined on capturing the unlikely and unexpected trio of a two-pound roach, one-pound dace and a five-pound chub from the same session on the Bristol Avon. The proverbial Cheshire Cat would have looked miserable sat next to me that night!

This is documented in an article I wrote in the February 2006 edition of *Improve Your Coarse Fishing*, the text reproduced here with the consent of the publisher.

> *"Snow and hard frosts had stripped the colour from the Bristol Avon but despite a biting wind the air temperature had just lifted after a longish spell of intense cold.*
>
> *Surely this would bring some fish on to feed.*
>
> *I turned off the computer early and headed for a deeper stretch of Chippenham AC's water where it carried more murk than the crystal clear shallows.*
>
> *Carrying two light quivertip rods, each equipped with fine line and feeders to present breadflake over mashed bread, I cast into a likely-looking near-side eddy. I was right about the rising temperature.*

Roach from 'razor blades' to 1lb were in a feeding frenzy, to the extent that I stowed away my second rod rather than constantly miss bites.

The streamy water under the opposite bank looked tempting, so I made an exploratory cast. The stronger current bore the feeder downstream before the rod tip dropped back, I settled the rod in the rest with just a slight bend in the quivertip.

Light was fading fast; enter the 'witching hour' when roach prime and feed…

Suddenly, the quivertip bucked and soon I was netting a fat dace of a dozen ounces. Quite unexpected but very welcome.

I re-baited and cast to the faster water and was rewarded with several more impressive dace.

Re-baiting and casting again, my next strike was met by a slightly more solid resistance. Not the shake of a chub, the bore of a barbel, nor the kick of a roach, but a series of excited tremors. I played the mystery fish carefully on soft hands.

Soon she was in the net, a big female dace heavy with spawn and weighting 1lb!

I took a few more smaller roach, dace and gudgeon, and was having a glorious time. Twenty minutes later, I bent into a stronger force.

This fish was less keen on coming to the net. I bided my time, exerting a forgiving pressure as the fish thumped and kited. In a couple of minutes, the flank of a hefty roach glinted over the rim of my landing net.

At two ounces over the magical two-pound barrier, it was bigger than any I had caught on this stretch of river for 10 years.

The fish was quite hollow and somewhat hunched with age though, surprisingly for early February, had already begun to form the characteristic head nodules of a male roach in spawning livery. How heavy would it be in good condition?

I share with Richard Walker the view that a 1lb dace and a 2lb roach in a sitting is one of the pinnacles of angling. Quite by chance, I'd 'done' the great man's 'magic double' for the fourth time in two decades. All this on a chill winter's evening!

As the light faded, a circumspect nod of the tip was greeted by the thud of a chub.

I looked to see where it might bolt in the clear water; the raft of debris downstream was an obvious refuge. I sapped the chub's energy against my light tackle out in the clear mid-river where there were fewer bolt-holes. Slowly, very slowly, it began to tire against my steady pressure.

I offered the chub the net with the handle fully extended. It bolted, boring towards the flotsam as I swung the rod low to exert maximum side-strain. This was going to be tight!

Fortunately, I'd calculated right – just! – and the chub swung just short of the debris. It bucked and bored on, though each time the light rod arched a little less alarmingly. At last it porpoised to the surface, took in a mouthful of air, rolled on its side, and wallowed into the net.

I zeroed the scales, this time watching the needle pull round to five pounds and four ounces. A very decent fish from the upper Bristol

Avon! I slipped her back, not bothering to recast, and just sat a moment watching the evening gather in around me.

What a session! But what did one call this remarkable bag? Borrowing from the Walker, I named it the 'magic triple'.

Planned or just plain lucky, I count myself blessed and reflect now on that special trio of platinum bar, red-finned perfection and broad bronze flank.

A 'magic triple' indeed!"

You will go mad if you try to replicate this feat; I certainly have not and am just pleased to have been in luck that fateful evening. The best advice is to do as I did; go out on a bitterly cold day with no real expectation of anything much, stick with it, and wait for Lady Luck to smile upon you too!

Club, river and regional records

We will turn to British Records shortly, but first let's pause to consider other local records. These are important. Not because the holding of one confers fame, fortune or even proves any great angling virtue beyond sheer dumb luck! (We need only scan the British Record list for many holders past and present to prove this fact.) No, simply because it sets the benchmark for what is possible in one's locality. For most of us, certainly myself, time spent fishing is infinitely preferable to time spent driving, so the local context of specimen angling and the setting of realistic goals and expectations is of greater importance than fishing for the ultimate, often individually-known specimen.

One such fish fell to my line on 4th March 1990, a bitterly cold day with the Hampshire Avon up and brown. I unaccountably found that I had a prime stretch of river to share with only one other angler, soon to be my witness! This stretch of the middle Avon is renowned for big dace, which were backing up onto the shallow gravel runs for spawning. I had trotted my breadflake down the 'crease' of an eddy behind an island for the best part of an hour-and-a-half with a few decent roach and dace already showing. Wallis-casting out into mid-river, I held back the heavy loafer against the flow, the bulk shot walking the bait along the bed of the stream where heavy balls of mashed bread loose feed were trickling to entice the fish. I worked the float over unseen, submerged obstructions with fine thumb pressure on the rim of my centrepin reel. Suddenly, the float buried, and I tightened into a lively resistance that sought the faster flow. The thrill of a running dace imparts a characteristic feeling through nylon, carbon fibre and cork, and I knew this was a decent dace. With steady pressure, it slid to net, and only then did I realise quite how 'decent' it was! In fact, it was the biggest dace I had then ever seen, a plump soft-flanked female fish filled with spawn. In some amazement, I zeroed the scales and my witness and I watched the fish pull them to 1lb 4oz 8dr. A staggering fish by any stretch of the imagination, and as silver as any sea trout.

We photographed the fish as quickly as possible, letting her back into the flow with minimal stress or harm for she was surely on the very brink of spawning. As we chatted upon watching her shimmy off into the darkening waters as dusk crept over the riverscape, we agreed to round down the weight to the nearest ounce. 1lb 4oz would do! In due course, on reporting it to the angling press (ironically it won *Fish of the Week* contest for which I won a carp reel which would have been wholly impractical for dace fishing!) and claiming the Ringwood Angling Association and Hampshire Avon records, I realised that the British record was in fact 1lb 4oz 4dr... Doh! But the fish was safely back in the water, and the agreement I had reached with the witness was an agreement we decided to keep. As I write in 2011, both club and river record still stand after more than two decades. I do, however, believe that both are vulnerable, such is the promise and mystery of that most marvellous of rivers, the Hampshire Avon!

When I started work with the National Rivers Authority shortly after it was set up, I had to up sticks from my home by the Hampshire Avon and move to the West Country. I was going to miss the Hampshire Avon, but was ready for a new angling challenge. When seeking a new home, I focused in upon the Bristol Avon, and have never regretted that switch of Avons despite the fond place that the broad chalk downland landscape of the Hampshire Avon has in my heart. This Bristol Avon was a different prospect entirely, rising on limestone yet rapidly flowing onto heavy clays which give the river system a different, flashier character in winter and turn it into a series of near-static 'canals' between weirs during the dry months of summer. Some learning was required, and I set about my task with enthusiasm!

I had made some wrong assumptions about the Bristol Avon, and one of them was that I would have to set my specimen angling sights a lot lower. In fact, within the first few years I had taken eight of the river's (and region's) records. Although dace, or at least big dace, are few and far between on the Bristol Avon, I did indeed find some pockets of mightily impressive fish. On 21st November 1993, I had the good fortune to equal the previous Bristol Avon river record dace with a super fish of 13oz 8oz taken on bread trotted under a stick float with freezing fog hugging the river valley all day.

A somewhat younger and clean-shaven Mark gazes incredulously at the 1lb 4oz (and 8dr!) dace that holds the Ringwood Angling Association record and the Hampshire Avon River Record... but not the British crown!

Mark's November 1993 (former) record-equalling 13oz 8dr dace from the Bristol Avon.

189

And then, on 7th January 1996, I went a huge step further with a spawn-laden female dace of a staggering 1lb 2oz 8oz. The capture of this fish was all the more enjoyable for being caught 'properly': trotted out with breadflake from a fast run in the cloudy and rising Bristol Avon on a long float rod and ancient centrepin reel. This fish was not so silvery as many dace, almost brownish in hue. (Perhaps it was in fact a graining?) Anyhow, it took the Bristol Avon river record and the regional record, and I think it won me a rod from the weekly angling press too!

Mark's January 1996 Bristol Avon and regional river record dace of 1lb 2oz 8dr, a huge fish!

This was to be followed by another Bristol Avon record-equalling dace of 1lb 2oz 8dr taken on 17th January 2009, which was also to be the biggest dace reported from UK waters throughout the whole 2008-2009 season. However, this was no 'ordinary record' for it was a male fish, characterised by the tubercles beginning to develop around its head in anticipation of spawning. Comparing the upper (record male) fish in the photograph with the gravid 12oz female below, it is likely that a female of equivalent body size to the male but laden with eggs at this time of year would have weighted in at between 1lb 9oz and 1lb 10oz! This thoroughly vindicated the estimates of three or four fish that my regular fishing buddy and I had spotted and hunted over the years. Needless to say we never saw one on the bank!

Mark's January 2009 Bristol Avon river record-equalling male dace of 1lb 2oz 8dr (the top fish); a true monster!

British Records past and present

In the Collins Guide to The Freshwater Fishes of Britain and Europe, Bent J. Muus and Preben Dahlstrom correctly note that,

> *"...the capture of large dace requires considerable angling expertise."*

This is absolutely the case for the capture of these slim leviathans on a consistent basis; surely the test of true specimen angling. However, when it comes to individual record specimens, Lady Luck plays a far bigger part than many amongst us might like to admit, and particularly so for a mobile, shoaling species like the dace. As noted when considering local records, the capture of a record is no automatic proof of one's skill and nor does it ensure one's immortality! A few dace have held the formal status of 'British Record', though it is worth noting that the succession of dace records has been a lot less frequent than for many other species of fish.

Today, record fish are verified and recorded by the British Record (Rod Caught) Fish Committee (BRFC). The BRFC was formed in 1957, with the founding secretary, Peter Tombleson, serving until the demise of the National Anglers Council and his retirement in 1991. The BRFC puts in place strict procedures to be followed in claiming a record, which assure the precise identity and witnessing of both capture and weight of the potential record fish.

Although the list maintained by the BRFC has been unbroken since 1957, there was a challenge to this 'official' list of freshwater fishes in 1982 following a revision by the BRFC to disallow some historic record fish for which the evidence was equivocal. Unhappy with the revised list, the National Association of Specimen Groups (NASG) created its own 'breakaway' list for record freshwater fishes. These two rival lists coexisted uneasily for eight years, until common sense prevailed and agreement was reached in 1990 to combine both lists under the BRFC.

Whilst some pre-existing record fish were taken forward into the BRFC list when the organisation was formed in 1957, the former dace record was amongst the casualties of the application of consistent standards of evidence. Previous record lists were far less formal, often verified on little more than the word of the captor. In that light, written some years before the 'spring cleaning' of prior records by the BRFC, the following extract from E. Marshall-Hardy's 1942 book *Coarse Fish* is, to say the least, interesting:

> *"THE RECORD ROD-CAUGHT DACE was taken in September, 1932, from a tributary of the Hampshire Avon by Mr. R. W. Humphrey, and weighed 1 lb. 8 oz. 5 dr., a magnificent specimen, the authenticity of which has not, to my knowledge, been assailed…*

Other fine specimen Dace:

Dec.	1933.	River Penk.	Mr. J. S. Upton	1 lb. 7½ oz.
Jan.	1934.	River Mole.	Mr. F. W. Arnold	1 lb. 7½ oz.
Jan.	1934.	River Welland.	Mr. W. Smith	1 lb. 6½ oz.
	1910.	River Gade.	Mr. S. Corley	1 lb. 6½ oz.
	1905.	River Beane.	Mr. R. Robinson	1 lb. 6 oz.

*This, like other lists in this book, might be much extended, but the
fish detailed must suffice for our present purpose."*

Eminent fish biologist Alwyne Wheeler adds in his classic 1969 book *The Fishes
of the British Isles and North West Europe* that,

"The British record fish (1932) weighed 1 ½ lb (0.68 kg)."

The R.W. Humphrey fish is also asserted as the record by W E Davies in his 1971
(5th edition) book *The Technique of Freshwater Fishing and Tackle Tinkering*,

*"Caught by R W Humphrey from a tributary of the River Avon
(Hants.) in 1932, which weighed 1lb. 8ozs. 5drms."*

In his 1966 book *Small Stream Fishing*, David Carl Forbes notes that,

*"…this record, held by R.W. Humphrey with a fish from a tributary of
the Hampshire Avon, has stood unchallenged since 1932. By any
standards a dace of 1 lb is a really exceptional dace, and all dace
above 8 oz are good fish."*

Peter Wheat too, in his 1975 book *Catch More Dace* sets out a range of interesting
notable dace captures, some replicating those above,

England				
1-8-5	R. W. Humphrey	Hants. Avon trib.	Sept	1932
1-8-0	B. Venables	Kennet	June	?
1-7-12	J. S. Upton	Penk	Dec	1933
1-7-8	F. W. Arnold	Mole	Jan	1934
1-7-8	S. Rolfe	Stour (Suffolk)	Feb	1962
1-5-0	R. Walker	Cam	July	1938
1-4-8	J. Gasson	Little Ouse	May	1961
1-4-4	J. Gasson*	Little Ouse	Feb	1960
1-4-0	V. Canning	Kennet	Dec	1964
1-4-0	H. Mason	Wye	July	1959
1-4-0	C. Graham	Herts, stream	Sept	1968
1-4-0	B. Kettle	Wensum	Aug	1970
1-4-0	S. Brennan	Wharfe	Oct	1972
1-4-0	A. R. Matthews	Beane	?	1899

* British record as then recognised by the British Record (rod-caught) Fish Committee.

Wales				
1-5-2	S. Wilson	Llynfi	July	1966
1-5-0	J. Cartwright	Cynon	?	1965

Ireland				
1-2-0	J.T. Henry**	Blackwater	Aug	1966
1-1-0	F. M. Hambleton	Blackwater	July	1968
1-1-0	M. Hill	Blackwater	Aug	1972
1-0-4	J. Casey	Blackwater	July	1967
1-0-0	J.T. Henry	Blackwater	Aug	1966
1-0-0	T. Skelton	Blackwater	Aug	1966

** Irish record as then recognised by the Irish Specimen Fish Committee.

However, if we are to believe William J Howes' account in his 1958 book *Dace: How to Catch Them*,

> *"Confusion has often been caused concerning extra big dace, and there will always be some doubts regarding dace records because of the close similarity between large dace and small chub... Nevertheless, there seems little doubt about Mr. S. Horsfield's record fish caught in 1947."*

Mr S. Horsfield's fish is recorded as 1lb 8oz 12dr, taken from the River Derwent. Howes goes on to record other notable dace that include not only the R.W. Humphreys (1lb 8oz 5dms) fish but also,

Weight:	lb.	oz.	Captor	Place
	1	7½	J. Upton	River Penk
	1	7½	F. Arnold	River Mole
	1	7	A. Hibbard	
	1	6½	S. Corley	River Gade
	1	6½	W. Smith	River Welland
	1	6	R. Robinson	River Beane

He also notes that, "*In recent years*", prize rods had been won with many dace, two of which included a fish of 1lb 5oz 13dr caught by a Mr B. Richardson.

Either bigger dace swam far more freely prior to the 1960s, or fish identification and the witnessing of weights were more questionable. Or perhaps the modern angler has not the skill and patience of his or her forebears?

However, the details of these older, now discredited 'records' is largely lost. So let us wind the clock forwards and look at the last two dace to enter the official British Record (Rod Caught) Fish Committee list.

J Gasson's 1lb 4oz 4dm dace

A stunning dace of 1lb 4oz 4dr, taken in February 1960 by J. L. Gasson from the Little Ouse River at Brandon where the river marks the Suffolk/Norfolk border in Thetford Forest, was one of the longest-running of all British coarse fish records.

It held British Record status for an unrivalled forty-two years, until toppled in 2002. The Little Ouse was in its day a classic big dace river, flowing from chalk and containing notable specimens of many species.

Unfortunately, little more detail nor any photograph of this fish seem to have survived to the present day.

Simon Ashton's 1lb 5oz 2dr dace from the River Wear

On 11th August 2002, Simon Ashton took an absolute monster of a dace of 1 lb 5oz 2dr (0.595kg) from the River Wear near Durham. This, bear in mind, in mid-summer when the fish would have recovered from spawning but had not yet had the chance to build up reserves and body weight for the spawning season six and more months ahead. Who knows how big a specimen it would have been by then?

Following management of historic pollution throughout the 1990s, the River Wear had been fast gaining a reputation as a venue for specimen-sized coarse fish, especially the waters within the City of Durham. A further sign of the general recovery of the river is an increasing run of migratory salmonid fish, with the river considered amongst the best sea trout rivers in the country.

I have spoken with Simon about this fish and the details of its capture. It fell to float-fished maggots in the city centre. Sadly, Simon's photograph of the fish has not survived. However, the fish was fully verified, and a fine capture it was too!

Fine catches of specimen dace

William J Howes (*Dace: How to Catch Them*, 1958) also notes,

> "...a fine brace taken from the old Lea which scaled 2 lb. 9½ oz.
> The late H. T. Sheringham took five dace on the fly (a Brunton's
> Fancy) from the River Kennet in 1906. Each of these fish scaled
> over a pound, the largest weighing 1 lb. 2½ oz."

Better yet to come?

If even a minority of the non-record giant dace noted previously in this chapter were authentic, and there is of course a high probability that many or most were, then the current dace record is clearly in considerable jeopardy!

What is also quite striking about the 'roll of honour' of notable and record fish is just how many have been caught out of the months when they could be expected to be at their peak weight. The Humphrey and Ashton fish, for example, were caught in September and August respectively, prior to any winter fattening. Whilst J Glasson's former record fish fell in February, the 'peak weight' window, the tables taken from Peter Wheat's book are striking. All the big fish taken from Wales and Ireland fell in July or August, whilst the English fish were taken in September, June, December, January, February, July, May, February, December, July, September, August, October and '?': almost none in the peak weight 'zone'!

Had any of those fish been taken when laden with roe later in the season, how big might they have been?

The Scottish Record

Although the British Record (Rod Caught) Fish Committee does not run a discrete list of Scottish coarse fish species, such lists are held informally. The dace is one of a number of coarse fish that was introduced and is now well established in a number of Scottish rivers, most notably the lower reaches of the Clyde and the Forth which are both home to huge shoals of dace which seem to have colonised the streamier waters rather quicker than the roach. Dace are also common on the Tweed, Endrick and Leven, and they are also present (and presumably still spreading) in other south-western and Borders rivers. There is no reason why these cold-adapted fish should not thrive in northern British rivers.

The Scottish record dace at the time of writing is a fine fish of 1 lb 3oz 8dr (0.553kg) taken from the River Tweed at Coldstream, by G. Keech in 1979.

Your next bite…

It really could be you next for the record, you know, and judging by the lists above it could come at any time of year too! Although the capture of big fish on a consistent basis by design is a skilled art, the history books are laden with 'fluked' record fish and long may that honourable tradition remain.

I have stalked outstanding dace well above the British record with an angling colleague over the past years. One Bristol Avon fish in particular we reckoned to be about 1lb 9oz in summer livery, and this a fish seen many times right under our rod tops in clear water but never with much of an appetite. Another fish that we stalked was at least 1lb 8oz but far more difficult to approach in a different stream no more than four feet wide, and some miles away from the other Bristol Avon monster. Our efforts were not rewarded, at least not with the individual fish we were pursuing by sight, but the pursuit is everything and the capture might just be anticlimactic if it puts to an end many years of hoping and trying! As I write, there are two other shoals of dace including fish over the British record which have caught our attention, my mate having had fish to 1lb 6oz from one of them in years gone by before he knew where the record stood!

Actually, there are probably more 'record' dace caught than potential records for any other species (apart from silver bream). A bold statement, granted, but one backed up not only by my own experiences but also those of various of my fishing colleagues. Generally, the tales break down into two categories. Firstly, they were not quite sure if it was a dace as it looked too big. Secondly, they knew it was a biggie, but had no idea what the record was or what to do next!

The simple advice on the latter is to get reliable witnesses, as many as possible but at minimum two that are not related to you. Then, get them to witness the whole weighing process and get them to help you take as many good quality photos as possible with close-ups of key identification features (lateral line, extended anal and dorsal fins, and mouth area). Phone an angling weekly magazine (they have 'hot-lines' accessible 24/7) and they will take over the formal process on the promise of an 'exclusive'. I could relate the whole rigmarole of contacting and processing a claim through the British Record (Rod Caught) Fish Committee (as I did in *The Complete Book of the Roach*), but the guidance above will get you what you need at the time. Then put the fish back carefully once you have assured yourself that the photos, identification and witnessed weighing are fine. Then take your witnesses for a drink!

Strong year classes

For all fishes, there is considerable variation in survival from spawning between years. Typically, for our cyprinid fish, a cool summer means that fewer fry grow large and strong enough to survive winter spates. Poor preceding winter weather may also contribute by limiting the richness of yolk laid down in eggs. Some years may see survival of fry failing completely. The net result is substantial variability in the strength of different 'year classes' of fish in the river.

Although this effect is less pronounced for the cold-adapted dace than other river cyprinids, there may from time to time be a generation of huge fish in the river. When they are there, fish for them! Shorted-lived as dace are, these prime fish may well not be there the next year. There is just no telling when the next classic year might happen. If you are lucky enough to encounter such a superlative year class in your river, make hay whilst the sun shines!

'Big dace' rivers

So where do you go for that elusive giant dace? There are many classic dace rivers, from Hertfordshire's tiny River Beane, northwards to the River Tyne and County Durham's River Wear, eastwards to Norfolk's Thet and Little Ouse, westwards to the Dee and Wye, and southwards to the Kennet, the Evenlode, the Wandle, the Hampshire Avon and many besides. The Derbyshire Derwent too is reputed a fine dace river, though much of it is cleared of 'vermin' fish to make way for their stately, adipose-bearing brethren considered by some as superior regardless of their dubious genetic or even farmed provenance As 'A Regular Rod' writes in the Winter 2006 edition of *Waterlog* magazine,

> *"It was a long time ago. I don't suppose it matters if I divulge Chatsworth's secret treasure that I found one winter; whilst strett-pegging behind an aged, sawn down, alder slump, which acted like a natural croy in the flow. The treasure? Dace! Very big dace indeed...*

> *"Three of the dace caught would each have been eligible for the British Rod Caught Record, which was, and still is under 1lb 6oz. And these whoppers were by no means alone. There were others, all over the one-pound mark, specimens every one of them. They all ate bread paste very confidently, which was just as well, because your correspondent would have caught nowt if they'd been difficult!"*

However, you would be foolhardy to focus only on classic rivers, or indeed upon larger streams. As David Carl Forbes notes of dace in his 1966 book *Small Stream Fishing*,

> *"Dace, trout and perch are all admirably suited to the small-stream environment. They thrive in suitable waters, and while other species must be considered in relation to fish from larger waters, there is every chance that these fish, particularly trout and perch, will be as big and be in as good, if not better condition, than fish from any other type of water."*

I can only concur, being an avid dabbler in ditches and a boy bewitched by brooks. Many hold mysteries of fish both diverse and, on occasion, surprisingly huge! How many classic dace do we fail to locate simply because we dismiss small streams as insignificant?

A world record?

According to the website www.fishing-worldrecords.com (accessed November 2010), the world record for the dace is over 2lb. Two fish are listed.

The largest fish for which a photograph is available (albeit that the head of the fish is missing from the photograph) is reported to have fallen in 1982 to the rod of F. Gruenauer from a 'pond near Cologne, Germany' weighting in at a massive 0.95 kilogrammes (2lb 2oz) with a length of over 40 centimetres (over 16 inches). Though the head of the fish can not be seen in the image, what is visible looks credible.

However, the web site lists an even bigger rod-caught dace of 1.10 kilogrammes (2lb 7oz) taken from France in a year reported as '200_'. This leviathan was reported to scale 45 centimetres (18 inches) in length. It is a shame that lack of photographic evidence, as well as a shortage of other supporting details, casts doubt on the veracity of this claim.

And finally…

Size, as they say, is not everything! It is a bold ambition and a worthy quest to catch large fish by design, but never let that deflect you from enjoying each and every dace you catch. It is a joy sometimes just to put the targets and intentions to one side and just take a light rod to the river to catch dace!

And, even if the dace are not feeding, it a joy to spend time by flowing water, where vole and dabchick paddle the margins and time expands so that we feel perhaps more alive than at any other time. It is never about waiting patiently for the next fish, big or small, either. As Arthur Ransome wrote in his delightful 1929 book *Rod and Line*,

> *"Patience is a virtue required when time goes slowly. In fishing time goes too fast."*

To this, Chris Yates adds in his 2006 book *How to fish*,

> *"I never wear a watch and, anyway, our perception of time as an orderly sequence or regular ticks and tocks has no relevance here in the alternative dimension that is fishing."*

So enjoy it all, every tiddler and every moment with rod in hand. Above all, don't let the disease of 'bigness' infect you whilst you undertake the quest for the biggest of these little fish out there; enjoy all the precious moments regardless of outcome! I will leave the last word on this matter to the late, great Richard Walker in two extracts from the second edition (1975) of his classic *Stillwater Angling*,

> *"The notion that a carp of 20lb 1oz is a great triumph while one of 19lb 15oz is a mere tiddler of which its captor should be ashamed, is manifestly ridiculous. We have come to a pretty pass in standard-setting if our pleasure is dependent on whether or not a fish drops an ounce or two of shit on its way to the landing net."*

> *"I am proud to say that I don't know how many fish eligible to be considered as 'specimens' I have caught. All I know is that I enjoyed the surroundings in which they were caught, and I hope to go on enjoying all this till I die. Which is more, I know why I enjoy it."*

Reflections on dace angling

If you hanker after bigness, in a world hooked on the pursuit of bigness for the sake of bigness, then you would not have read this far. So welcome to you, Brother of the Angle! Dace are wild spirits of sharp flows and untamed waters, though they can often thrive in spite of society's seeming best intentions to strangle our rivers.

The grayling is said to be the 'coarse game fish', a sometimes maligned though elegant salmonid species that is nevertheless covered by coarse fishing seasons due to its springtime spawning. It is then as surely true that the dace is the 'game coarse fish' so lithe is it in the flow, eager to take the fly, and sprightly in the fight. A gamer small bar of silver, as keen to take a bait under a blazing sun or a withering frost, is hard or impossible to find.

I don't know any angler who does not like dace, although I know plenty who have forgotten that these little fish and the places that they inhabit can bring so much pleasure. In fishing for dace, the self-hooking rig has no place. One has instead to find them in the livelier flows that they favour, adapt one's approach accordingly, be stealthy and subtle, and remain reactive as quicksilver if one wishes with any constancy to capture good dace by design. A fish then to hone the instincts of a true angler!

Though few writers have summed up succinctly what it is to dace fish, many have said wise words about fishing itself. Of simply being there, the oft-quoted Abyssinian inscription of 3,000 BC takes some beating,

> *"The Gods do not take away from a life the time one spends in fishing."*

Determining who is or who is not such a true angler is a task not for humankind. Rather, it is when the patrolling kingfisher, the strafing sparrowhawk, the bank-top fox, the ever-vigilant dabchick and the hawking dragonfly sense you merely as another facet of the bustling world of which they too are integral parts. Then, and only then, is one of the place and stillness that can be called 'fisherman', and perhaps your float top too will nod in quiet acquiescence.

Of the waiting, the wisdom of Richard Walker on the matter of angling patience – specifically the comment during his Desert Island Discs radio appearance that what the angler actually requires is controlled impatience – is recognised by many anglers. However, Arthur Ransome pre-empted this sentiment many years previously, stating nicely in his 1929 book *Rod and Line* that,

> *"What other people mistake for patience in anglers is really nothing of the sort but a capacity for prolonged eagerness, an unquenchable gusto in relishing an infinite series of exciting and promising moments, any one of which may yield a sudden crisis with its climax of triumph or disaster."*

Nevertheless, if dace did grow to large sizes, say 10-12lb, just imagine what fantastic sport they – or indeed 'double figure' bleak or minnows – would give us? We would have no need to lust after mahseer or comizo barbel in foreign climes, having our own freshwater torpedoes eagerly succumbing to fly, float, ledger or freeline, and probably to lures and live baits as well.

Dace are, however, a small species. We should think no lesser of them for that genetic reality; rather we should admire them all the more for their perfect adaptation of form to lifestyle.

Beauty is so often in the eye of the beholder, and many are the anglers who find beauty in the elegant dace. John Bailey evoked this wonderfully in his 1984 book *In Visible Waters* when speaking of a particular dace caught during a lingering sunset on a bitterly cold day on Norfolk's River Nar,

> *"The birds were already in the barebone wood – everything else had burrowed in for a dire night – when I caught a dace. At that moment, it was the most obliging, beautiful thing I could ever have*

hoped to see. It was as silver as the stars, it twinkled as bright as the frost, and then as I held it in my hand and the sun's last rays caught it, the scales turned to rose and flame. It was as beautiful and as worthy a fish as I have ever seen and one that would be impossible to re-create if ever lost."

Of the Prince of the Stream, the sentiment expressed by Arthur P Bell in his 1930 book *Fresh-water Fishing for the Beginner* cannot be improved upon,

"A JOLLY little fish if ever there was one."

This book is written for the jolly little angler that resides still in all of us!

Dace: The Prince of the Stream

Dace:
The Prince of the Stream

Part III. Dace and people

Dace and people

We have co-evolved with dace, both as two species inhabiting the same changing landscape as well as in terms our developing culture. Inevitably, we will have shaped each other and also been moulded collectively by the same external forces. It is an inescapable conclusion that we owe dace a greater duty of care than we have offered them to date in the ways that we have used the natural world around us and degraded the environments that sustain them, and which we ultimately depend upon to sustain ourselves into the longer-term future. Notwithstanding the vulnerability of dace to the pressures we place on the natural world, this third section of the book is concerned with the unbreakable if often unappreciated interrelationship of dace and people.

Dace as a food fish

Various members of the carp or minnow family (*Cyprinidae*), particularly the common carp (*Cyprinus carpio*) but also many other species, are widely used as a protein source by people. Some have significant economic importance. In his 1969 book *The Fishes of the British Isles and North West Europe*, Alwyne Wheeler, notes of dace that,

> *"They are too small and bony to have any food value, but make a good bait for larger fish."*

However, dace are caught and consumed across continental Europe using both generic capture methods and as by-catches when fishing for other more 'mainstream' food fishes. Such dace catches nevertheless contribute to the overall local economy as well as availability of protein.

Dace as a sporting fish

It is a sporting fish that the dace contributes most to the economy, at least in the UK.

Alwyne Wheeler, again from *The Fishes of Great Britain and North West Europe* notes of the dace that,

> *"Dace have considerable value as angling fish, for although small they fight well on light tackle.   Their consistent capture is a demonstration of angling finesse, for their bite is light and swift and they are easily frightened."*

The democratic weight and economic force of angling are great.   There are anything between three-and-a-half and six million anglers in the United Kingdom. The best part of three million of these live in England and Wales, and 79% (approaching 2.5 million) of these angle for coarse fish.

Of course, dace feature as only one of a suite of species of interest to these people, and for a minority of them only as a bait for pike and other predatory fishes. However, add to this potential democratic force the fact that the angling economy of England and Wales is estimated at £3 billion, roughly equivalent to the £3.2 billion estimated as derived from agriculture, and the economic and potentially political might of angling is revealed.

At a more local scale, dace are just one of a mix of fish species that attract anglers to different localities where they can make a surprisingly significant contribution to local livelihoods. Pubs and hotels, tackle shops and camp sites, village stores and post offices, restaurants and bed-and-breakfast businesses, garages and even local police forces all benefit from angling tourism on popular rivers. Some of the various British regional river trusts which constitute the Association of River Trusts have been clever in seeking funding for river enhancement works on the basis of their potential to boost regional economies, and have produced compelling cost-benefit analyses of the outcomes of their river restoration work for whole local communities.

And then, of course, we have to bear in mind the importance of aquatic ecosystems, whether or not the general public are familiar with them, in shaping public policy and investment in the quality of river environments.

Dace and the environment

The water quality requirements of both coarse and game fishes form the basis for the river classification schemes that have been used to support private and public investment in pollution control since the 1970s. It is a moot point as to whether, in the absence of fisheries, public awareness of and motivation to invest in the underwater world would be strong enough to drive the levels of investment in the maintenance or improvement of river quality that we see today.

Since the 1990s, 'environmentally-acceptable flows', reflecting the needs of fish and other elements of the ecosystems of which they are part, have also been part of a wider dialogue informing regulation of water abstraction. The role of dace and other freshwater fish in curbing human over-exploitation of natural resources, with all of the unwanted costs and declining 'quality of life' that accrue from a degraded environment, is therefore as significant as it is under-appreciated.

In addition, the presence of thousands or millions of 'eyes and ears' on the bank, in the shape of concerned anglers and nature-lovers, creates an informal national network of vigilance concerned about the quality of our rivers. This in turn provides intelligence upon which bodies such as the Environment Agency may act to investigate pollution and other forms of ecological damage, bringing about statutory prosecutions as necessary.

Where harm has occurred to fisheries, including the ecosystems that sustain fish stocks, Fish Legal (formerly the Anglers' Conservation Association or ACA) is a powerful non-governmental body active since 1948 in fighting pollution and other harm to waters by using common law to recover often significant damages from those responsible for causing it.

Other bodies interested in river restoration significantly include the River Restoration Centre (RRC), the Wild Trout Trust (WTT) and the network of local catchment-based river trusts now under the umbrella of the Association of River Trusts (ART). These organisations are renowned for their 'wet welly' work of restoring degraded habitat in rivers to support aquatic ecosystems. Dace are both one of the driving forces and net beneficiaries of this up-welling of public concern and activism.

All of these measures, of course, support more than just dace and, indeed, more than just fish. Environmental protection and enhancement benefit everything from otters to dippers and kingfishers, water voles, dragonflies and sedge flies, sand martins, water crowfoot (*Ranunculus*) and other aquatic and emergent vegetation, freshwater shrimps, crayfish and the whole wide ecosystem.

This is, of course, desirable of itself. However, a healthier river will in turn do more of those things performed by rivers in their natural state, including retention of floodwater and its slow release in times of lower rainfall, improved exchange with groundwater, chemical purification of the water itself, more dependable flows of clean water for domestic or agricultural use, greater dilution to render effluent safe, self-generating fisheries, areas of natural beauty and quiet recreation, and a host of other often unappreciated natural functions that deliver real public benefits of massive cumulative economic value. Healthy dace populations indicate more than just good fishing. They speak of lively flows, diverse habitats and thriving ecosystems which deliver a wet wealth to society as a whole, and can better support more of our needs. Dace stocks, in short, are crucial parts of our sustainable future.

Dace and the economy

Yes, dace make some contribution to the economics of commercial fishing across continental Europe, but their part within the recreational economy is most significant. However, the economy is about more than what is directly bought and sold. It is also about cultural values, which in turn influence private and public investment decisions regarding our perceived 'quality of life'.

It is in this latter context that the contribution of dace, other freshwater fishes and representative elements of aquatic ecosystems are the most significant. So the environmental protection and restoration measures afforded to the habitat and general environmental requirements of dace, overlapping with acknowledged clean-water species such as brown trout, form probably an even greater contribution to the overall economy. We also have to factor in to the balance sheet the substantial value of healthy ecosystems, landscapes and their associated fisheries to the overall tourist economy, which generally exceeds that of agriculture quite significantly. It is plain that fish and their needs influence investment and returns from very big sums of money.

There was often a myopia amongst game angling interests. Some anglers and river keepers historically held a negative attitude about coarse fish and anything else that is not silver and spotty. For example, John Ashley-Cooper says of the upper Avon in his 1985 book *A Ring of Wessex Water* that,

> *"Coarse fish, such as chub, roach, and dace are only a minor problem on this part of the river... It is difficult to assess the amount of damage which they do. They are present in all chalk rivers, as well as in other waters, and no doubt devour quantities of sub-surface food which would otherwise be available to trout... Eels are unpleasant creatures and so far as one knows do no good... Herons are a permanent hazard... Other birds can be a nuisance... Cormorants have no redeeming features... Coarse fish are not a problem anywhere in the Ebble except in the lowest reaches..."*

And so it goes on! This is hardly reflective of the natural balance of rivers, which we have come more recently to realise as being of overwhelming importance. There are, of course, conflicts to be managed. For example, in discussing dace, Alwyne Wheeler states in *The Fishes of the British Isles and North West Europe* that,

> *"Their presence in numbers in salmon streams is probably a disadvantage as they compete with the parr for food, though to what degree has not been clearly determined."*

The coarse angler in me says that maybe the salmon parr compete for food with dace too! However, the important point here is that, for a species as endangered as the salmon, careful planning of river protection and enhancement work needs to take place to ensure that salmon can prosper in habitat best suited to the specific needs of vulnerable life stages, within a matrix of habitats along the river wherein they may coexist in balance with other elements of the ecosystem and which support other of their needs throughout their own life histories.

Dace and science

Studies of dace have advanced our knowledge of various branches of science. As referred to in *Part I* of this book, the physiological requirements of dace – oxygen concentrations, swimming speeds, temperature preferences and tolerances, and so forth – and those of other fishes have helped us understand the world around us to a far better extent. This knowledge in turn has shaped the way in which we control pollution, manage aspects of abstraction both directly from rivers and from the groundwaters that naturally feed them, protect or enhance habitat, and shape land usage to allow rivers to function naturally.

Dace have also been the subject of studies about the mechanisms and pace of evolution. For example, they have featured in studies of the complex of dace species across Continental Europe. Dace show five distinct lineages across their European range. These scientific studies are aided by the very wide geographic distribution of *Leuciscus leuciscus* right across the continent, where their common occurrence also makes them ideal study animals for variation in morphology (meristic characters), genetics and biochemistry.

Dace and technology

It would be easy to labour this one! Suffice to say that the global tackle industry is huge and the economics of angling in the British Isles are significant by any standard, as outlined already. The pursuit of dace and other fish species of match, pleasure and/or specimen angling interest adds to the innovation of the technology of fishing rods, reels, fishing lines, bait, hooks and other paraphernalia, a surprising amount of it deriving from materials technology developed to support space, arms and motor sport industries. The precise magnitude to which dace contribute to tackle technology is uncertain, but they certainly have a part to play in the overall picture.

Dace and social wellbeing

This title may sound a little far-fetched, but it is not. In recent years, the contribution of angling activities for promoting social inclusion and public engagement with the natural environment have begun to be studied and appreciated. This contribution is substantial, and is one of the key political levers driving the continued support of the British government for the promotion of angling.

Angling gatherings, be that national conventions, local committee meetings, matches, specimen groups or informal chats in the pub or on the river bank, all build the kind of social cohesion that is sadly in decline in a consumerist, 'me first' society where computer games, addiction to television and fear of crime drive people to engage in solitary and not communal activities.

It is my view, and that of many of my peers, that closeness with nature, an unavoidable consequence of angling, is of immense value in ingraining into children an appreciation of the natural world. This provides a platform that may shape their further development and adult sensibilities. Rivers and their denizens also provide invaluable educational resources, both in the formal sense and as a place for quiet reflection, appreciation and recreation throughout life.

Rivers with water clean enough and flows lively enough to support dace, be they urban or rural, can have an often overlooked importance in supporting regional and local regeneration. Proximity to such places certainly also boosts property values, both commercial and residential, to a significant extent. In conclusion, we commonly undervalue the place of healthy river ecosystems in sustaining social wellbeing, and we do so to our considerable long-term disadvantage.

To fish is good for the soul, reconnecting people to the natural world, making them fitter through exercise, and promoting healthy social interaction be that activism to protect the quality of the water, planning events and angling organisations, or just chatting about the mother of all dace that got away!

Where do dace get their name?

It is fascinating to conjecture where everyday words, which we take so much for granted, actually come from. Also, what names might have been used before the currently-accepted form came into general usage or vogue? Let's consider the case of the dace.

Why 'dace'?

The name 'dace' is, according to the *Concise Oxford Dictionary*, derived from the old French word Dars. Conrad Gessner (1516-1565), the Swiss naturalist whose three-volume *Historiae Animalium* (1555-1558) is considered the beginning of modern zoology, records that the fish we know today as the dace was called the Dard by the Santones and Pictones (the old names for the inhabitants of the provinces of Saintonge and Poitou), because the fish moves rapidly, like an arrow or 'dart'. (*"Alia Leucisci species est ea quse hodie a Gallis Vandoise vocatur, a Santonibus et Pictonibus Dard, quod sagittse modo sese vibret."*)

The dace is also known variously, across the UK and in old books, as the 'dare' or the 'dart'. The former of these alternative names clearly relates directly to the old French name. 'Dart' is generally thought to allude to the sprightly movements of the fish. However, like 'dace', the three words are fairly similar and are likely to have similar roots. The Reverend W. Houghton, in the 1879 book *British Fresh-Water Fishes*, notes that,

> *"The word Dace appears to have been formed by what philologists term 'phonetic decay' from the fuller form of dart, a name which, with another synonym of dare, is applied to the fish under our consideration."*

Opinions vary about the details of the derivation, but 'dace' it is for most of the residents of the British Isles today!

We must also remember the Lancashire name 'graining', formerly thought to be a separate species in that county but dismissed as such by the eminent ichthyologist C. Tate Regan around the beginning of the twentieth century. (The history of the graining is described in the opening chapter of *Part I* of this book.) Of the graining, or at least the fish of that name, the *Concise Oxford Dictionary* is silent.

However, there are other definitions of the word 'graining'. It is tempting to speculate that some of these meanings, for example the practice of imitating wood grain with paint or the roughening of a surface, might describe the bold scales of the dace or the roughness of a male fish prior to spawning. However, in all probability the derivation lies overseas as the graining, before its misidentification as a separate species was confirmed, was originally thought to be distributed mainly in continental Europe and particularly in the Mediterranean region.

Scientific names for the dace

The advantage of a consistent and agreed scientific name is that it not only aids us in knowing that we are talking about the same bug, beast or weed – just look at the possible confusion between British and American dace as one example – but that it also gives us clues about the relationship of species one to another. We are all doubtless familiar with the currently-accepted scientific Latin name for dace: *Leuciscus leuciscus*. However, this name has not been with us forever, and dace have been known by very many scientific names in ages past.

The modern two-part (or three-part if we are talking about sub-species) *binomial nomenclature* used for the Latin scientific names of species today is less than three-hundred years old itself, established by the Swedish scientist Carl von Linné (better known by the Latinate version of his name *Linnaeus*) in his great botanical work *Systema Natura* of 1735. This 'modern' naming convention classified plants (initially) into groups based upon shared characteristics. This superceded pre-existing scientific naming conventions which were often very long, describing in a great list the key biological characteristics of species. However, even under the Linnean (a term derived from *Linnaeus*) naming convention, the familiar dace has not always been known by the now-familiar Latin name *Leuciscus leuciscus*. Other Latin names by which it has been known over the years, including supposed separate species since proven to be none other than dace, include:

- *Cyprinus grislagine* Linnaeus, 1758
- *Cyprinus leuciscus* Linnaeus, 1758
- *Cyprinus dobula* Linnaeus, 1758
- *Leuciscus dobula* Linnaeus, 1758
- *Cyprinus graining* Walbaum, 1792
- *Cyprinus squalus* Walbaum, 1792
- *Cyprinus umbra* Walbaum, 1792
- *Cyprinus lancastriensis* Shaw, 1804
- *Cyprinus simus* Römer-Büchner, 1827
- *Leuciscus vulgaris* Fleming, 1828
- *Leuciscus argenteus* Fitzinger, 1832
- *Leuciscus majalis* Agassiz, 1835
- *Leuciscus rodens* Agassiz, 1835
- *Leuciscus rostratus* Agassiz, 1835
- *Cyprinus mugilis* Vallot, 1837
- *Leuciscus rostratus* Valenciennes, 1844
- *Leuciscus saltator* Bonaparte, 1845
- *Squalius chalybeius* Heckel, 1852
- *Squalius lepusculus* Heckel, 1852
- *Cyprinus salax* Gronow, 1854
- *Squalius vulgaris argenteus* Walecki, 1863
- *Squalius vulgaris* leptorhinus Walecki, 1863
- *Squalius vulgaris minor* Walecki, 1863
- *Squalius vulgaris robustior* Walecki, 1863
- *Squalidus baicalensis non* Dybowski, 1874
- *Squalius leuciscus elata* Fatio, 1882

- *Squalius leuciscus elongata* Fatio, 1882
- *Squalius leuciscus lateristriga* Fatio, 1882
- *Squalius suworzewi* Warpachowski, 1889
- *Squalius mehdem* Warpachowski, 1897
- *Leuciscus leuciscus baicalensis kirgisorum* Berg, 1912
- *Idus stagnalis* Dubalen, 1913
- *Leuciscus leuciscus baicalensis teletzkensis* Johansen, 1945
- *Leuciscus leuciscus roulei* Bertin & Estève, 1948

However, you won't be tested on this daunting list of names! *Leuciscus leuciscus* is about all you are ever likely to need to know for any practical purpose, as this is the standard to which all now agree. It is just instructive at times to look at how the science of taxonomy has evolved throughout the years, and to appreciate how incomplete and transient our current understanding may be about dace and life!

The dace in other languages

You may, like me, carry travel rods with you when venturing abroad on holidays or business. If so, the following names may be handy to know when speaking of your catches or hopes by other waters in which dace swim.

Oh, and don't forget all those other so-called 'dace' from the Americas which, though still members of the carp or minnow family (the *Cyprinidae*) are not really 'dace' at all, at least in European terms!

French	*Vandoise* (or alternatively *Vaudoise* in older French)
Dutch	*Serpeling*
German	*Hasel*
Danish	*Strømskalle*
Swedish	*Stäm*

Other meanings of the word 'dace'

Many of the common names of British freshwater fishes have other meanings ('chub', 'trout', 'roach', etc.) In some cases, these other meanings may explain the derivation of the name of the fish. Strangely, this is not the case for the dace, the common name for which arrived into the English language from the French, through phonetic decay or whatever route, all on its own. 'Dace' it is then!

Dace also lend their name to a small road in Hackney Wick, London E4, just south of the junction of the Hertford Union Canal with the River Lea Navigation. Water and its life forms define much of the area, which includes not only Dace Road but also Bream Street, Roach Road, Beachy Road and Stour Road (the common river name 'Stour' being, like 'Avon', 'Frome', 'Ouse', etc., derived from Celtic words for 'river').

Two American submarines have taken the name USS Dace. Both vessels were named after the group of several small North American freshwater 'dace' which, though members of the carp or minnow family (*Cyprinidae*), are not closely-related to the European dace.

The first of these, USS Dace (SS-247), was a 1526-ton Gato class submarine, built by the Electric Boat Company of Groton, Connecticut. It was commissioned in July 1943, serving in the Pacific from September 1943 through to the end of World War II. During this time, the USS Dace carried out seven war patrols, and was credited with sinking six sizable Japanese ships including the heavy cruiser *Maya*. USS Dace (SS-247) was taken out of commission from February 1947 until August 1951, after which time the USS Dace operated in the Atlantic during 1951-53 then underwent an extensive modernisation. After a brief period of active duty from October 1954 through to January 1955, she was transferred to the Italian Navy, where she

The submarine in the foreground is one of the few remaining images of USS Dace (SSN-247).

was renamed the *Leonardo da Vinci*. This submarine remained in Italian service until disposed of in 1972.

USS Dace (SSN-607) at sea.

The second dace-named American vessel, USS Dace (SSN-607), was a Permit-class nuclear submarine, constructed by Ingalls Shipbuilding in Pascagoula, Mississippi, from which she was launched in August 1962. Commissioned in April 1964, USS Dace (SSN-607) patrolled extensively throughout the Cold War, and was decommissioned and removed from the Naval Vessel Register in December 1988 and subsequently recycled in Washington State.

The word 'dace' also has another military meaning. The acronym DACE is an abbreviation for Data And Command Equipment.

And finally, to return from the military back to the streets of London, 'roach and dace' is an alternative and less common Cockney (London) 'rhyming slang' term for 'face'. However, 'boat race' and 'Chevy Chase' are now the most common rhyming slang terms used for the face. For those who don't already know, Cockney rhyming slang is one of the Cockney gifts to world culture, comprising a code of speaking in which common words are replaced by the whole or abbreviated phrases rhyming with that word. 'Roach and dace' for 'face', 'Lillian Gish' for 'fish', 'shake and shiver' for 'river', and so on. Rhyming slang has evolved in London's East End of London since the Sixteenth Century, and is still evolving, perhaps initially as a method to keep conversations secret from outsiders or for other reasons lost in the mists of time.

Dace on the menu

Up to the 1960s, the taking of coarse fish for the pot was the norm. Indeed, angling permits issued by River Boards across England and Wales (which seem quite recent to me but which were in fact abolished way back in 1971) stipulated minimum sizes of fish of different species that could be taken. So too the licenses issued by various regional Water Authorities that superseded them, persisting through to the privatisation of the water industry and the formation of the National Rivers Authority (NRA) in 1990.

Under British law current at the time of writing, coarse fish can still be taken. Ironically, migratory salmonid fish are now covered by catch-and-release bye-laws in various river catchments where the conservation of stocks is an over-riding priority. How the law swings in the balance of coarse versus game fish!

The fact remains that few people today take coarse fish for the table. Indeed, it is so unusual that there has been a media outcry in the UK at the taking of coarse fish by immigrant families from Eastern Europe and beyond where the eating of coarse fish is still an accepted norm.

The intent of this chapter is not to reverse the tendency to return all coarse fish from whence they were caught; it is written for both completeness and in part as a historical record.

First take your dace…

Dace are reported to be bony in texture, which puts many people off taking them for the table.

Not all authorities agree on the virtues of the flesh of dace. In *The Compleat Angler*, Izaak Walton talks of catching dace but, uncharacteristically, makes no comment about their culinary virtues. Meanwhile, Alwyne Wheeler notes, in his 1969 *The Fishes of Great Britain and North West Europe*, that,

> *"They are too small and bony to have any food value, but make a good bait for larger fish"*

The Reverend W. Houghton, in his classic book *British Fresh-Water Fishes* is less committal about the gastronomic virtues of the dace.

> *"They are in good condition in September and October, and though not held in great repute in a gastronomic point of view, being rather soft in flesh and full of small bones, fine specimens out of our clear rivers are not to be despised when nicely fried."*

However, there are a number of authors who positively rave about the gastronomic virtues of the dace (albeit acknowledging their boniness). For example, in his 1910 book *An Open Creel*, H.T. Sheringham notes that;

> *"It is worth while catching a dish of these little dace, if only for the pleasure of looking at them afterwards. They make a brave silvery show when laid side by side, and though individually at time of capture they have not the looks of brook trout, collectively in the*

evening they have the advantage. Brook trout lose their gold, but dace preserve their silver. One good angler informed me (rather apologetically), that he proposed to have his catch to breakfast. No apology was needed, for, bones admitted and extracted, dace are good meat — as good as many trout."

Preferences for different fish species as food are, however, as much polarised by cultural and religious differences as they are by the accessibility of a good meal. It is then unsurprising that the Reverend W. Houghton reports that,

"The Jews have a great liking for Dace, and indeed for white fish generally, and, as Mr. Manley says, they consume them in large numbers (at least when they can get them) during their fasts. Very fine Dace are said to be produced in the New River, near Hornsey, specimens of three-quarters of a pound being by no means uncommon; according to Mr. Pennell, the people residing in the neighbourhood are said to prefer them to Trout for the table."

Ways to cook dace

Remember, my personal recommendation is that you put your dace back having paused only long enough to admire the handsome *Prince of the Stream*. However, it is worth recording, if only for historical interest, what has been said about the cooking of dace.

E. Marshall Hardy, writing in the little book *Coarse Fish* published during the Second World War, says of the eating of dace,

"For me the principal usefulness of Dace is as bait for Pike, but for those who will eat them here is a recipe which makes them acceptable at table. Remove the scales and head, then clean the fish thoroughly and fry in butter. Serve with mustard sauce."

Across France and Austria, I have seen dace taken, along with every other fish species that swims, for the purpose of making a meal. The same is probably true across most of their continental European range to one extent or another. Talking with locals, and allowing for my limitations in the French and German languages, there seem to be two general recipes to which a mixed bag of small fish are subject, and this applies whether the fish are cooked whole or else are first gutted and beheaded.

1. Fry them whole in a little butter or oil; or

2. Make of them a stew with diced vegetables and serve, presumably spitting out bones as you eat.

Chacun a son goût!

Think Before Dining!

If you are thinking of taking dace for the table, do first check the acceptability with national legislation in place at the time, any more detailed local by-laws, the rules of the fishing association controlling the water, and the wishes of the riparian land owner.

The art of the dace

The great artists found inspiration in many places, from the nude human form to celestial bodies, from the sweep of a landscape to the light on clouds at sea, and from the play of light upon a pool of water lilies to a bowl of fruit. Many facets of the natural world have been captured lovingly by the classical artists. Sadly though, none that I have been able to discern have produced masterpieces of dace!

Despite this obvious shortfall in high art, a great deal of more modern masterpieces have been produced. Indeed, dace have found representation of great artistic merit in technical illustrations, evocations of angling quarry, wonderful drawings and paintings in their own right, and digital photo-composites.

It is valuable, informative and enlightening, to give space to some of the images of dace that have been my companions and inspirations throughout a lifetime in thrall to water. The images have their own voices, so I'll shut mine up now!

Dace woodcut from Francis Willughby's 1686 Willughby de Piscibus.

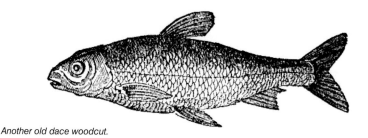

Another old dace woodcut.

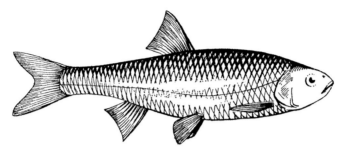

Dace drawing from E. Marshall-Hardy's Angling Ways (ninth edition, 1963).

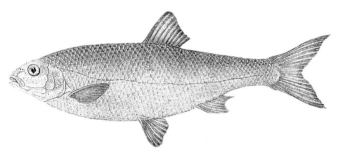

Dace, the prince of the stream, from Edward Donovan's 1804 book A Natural History of British Fishes.

A.F. Lydon's painting of dace and graining from The Reverend W. Houghton's classic 1879 book 'British Fresh-water Fishes'

A. Laurence Wells' painting of a dace from 'The Observer's Book of Freshwater Fishes of the British Isles' (1941).

Dace woodcut from E. Marshall-Hardy's 'Angling Ways' (ninth edition, 1963).

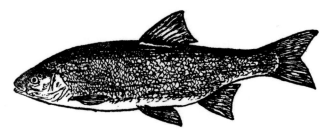

Dace drawing from William J. Howes' 'Dace: How to Catch Them' (1958).

Cover artwork from William J. Howes' Dace: How to Catch Them (1958).

Keith Linsell's painting on the cover of Peter Wheat's 1975 book Catch More Dace.

Bernard Venables' painting of dace feeding on flies from his 1993 book The Illustrated Memoirs of a Fisherman.

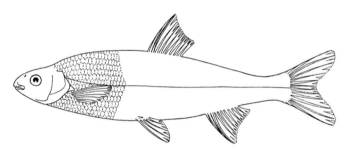

Valerie Du Heaume's scientific drawing of the dace from Alwyne Wheeler's 1969 book 'The Fishes of the British Isles and North West Europe'.

Dace painting by Jiří Malý from the 1968 book 'Freshwater Fishes'.

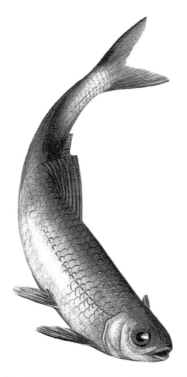

Dace painting from Alwyne Wheeler's 1969 book 'The Fishes of the British Isles and North West Europe'.

E.V. Petts' painting of a dace from the Brooke Bond Freshwater Fish tea card collection.

An excellent painting of two dace feeding by renowned angling artist Chris Turnbull that featured in the book The Anglers Guide To Freshwater Fish by John Wilson and Chris Turnbull (Boxtree Ltd, 1993).

Let us also not forget Mick Loates' wonderful painting of a dace that graces the cover of this book.

Perhaps to some, the illustrations throughout this book are also an art form!

Dace in literature

The great Elizabethan poet Michael Drayton (1563-1631) is reputed to have had in mind the 'darting' dace when he wrote the lines,

> *"Oft swiftly as he swims, his silver belly shows;*
> *But with such nimble flight, that ere ye can disclose*
> *His shape, out of your sight like lightning he is shot."*

However, other English literature dedicated solely to dace, whether prose, science, poetry or eulogy, is not going to trouble the storage capacity of the British Museum. Neither, it seems, do dace appear to have been the muse of any great musicians, though a former scientific colleague was wont to sing *"Happy dace are here again"* ad nauseum.

We are not, however, completely bereft of written words about the humble dace. Indeed, you will see that I have borrowed liberally from various of these published sources throughout this book.

Books about dace

There are, in fact, a handful of books on angling for dace, or at least dealing with dace as a major part of the work.

As far as I have been able to discover, only two other books deal exclusively with dace. Neither could be described, even generously, as very recent or comprehensive:

- Howes, William J. (1958). *Dace: How To Catch Them*. Herbert Jenkins, London.

- Wheat, Peter. (1975). *Catch More Dace*. Wolfe Publishing Ltd, London.

And then we have a handful of books in which dace are co-stars. These include:

- Bailey, John M. and Miller, Roger. (1990). *Chub and Dace*. The Crowood Press, Marlborough.

  (As I have discussed with John, dace only feature in the short final chapter *Days with dace*; four-and-a-half pages containing 2,210 words and no pictures. This just about edges ahead of the 2,152 words in Chapter 5, *Dace*, in John's 1984 book *In Visible Waters*. So, despite the consistently high quality of the writing in the Bailey library, there is yet more that could have been said about dace!)

- Bell, Henry. (1930). *Fly-fishing for Chub and Dace*. Simpkin, Marshall, Hamilton, Kent & Co.

- Edward Ensom ['Faddist']. (1953). *Roach and Dace Fishing*. Seeley, Service and Co. Ltd, Shaftesbury Avenue, London.

- Wilson, John. (1992). *Catch Roach, Rudd and Dace*. The Angling Times Library, Boxtree.

Books including dace

There are rather more books including mention of dace and the catching of them. Some cover the biology of the fish, others aspects of angling for them. I have no intention of repeating the quite comprehensive list in my previous book *The Complete Book of the Roach*, as many of the books I cite in that work cover dace as well as roach. Therefore, I will include the citation for my roach book below and also add to this a handful of other books simply because I like the way the dace is given due respect in their pages. Either that, or I simply enjoy them in their own right.

- Bailey, John M. (1984). *In Visible Waters*. The Crowood Press, Marlborough.

- 'BB' (Denys Watkins-Pitchford). (1943). *The Fisherman's Bedside Book*. (Republished in 2004 by the Merlin Unwin Books, Ludlow.)

- Bell, Arthur F. (1930). Fresh-water *Fishing for the Beginner*. Warne's 'Recreation'Books. F. Warne and Co. Ltd., London.

- Berners, Dame Juliana (Abbess of Shropshire). (1496). *The Treatysse of FysshyngeWith an Angle*. (Republished by the Medlar Press, Ellesmere.)

- Davies, W. E. (1971). (5th edition). *The Technique of Freshwater Fishing and Tackle Tinkering*. Paperfront, Kingswood, Surrey.

- Everard, Mark. (2006). *The Complete Book of the Roach*. Medlar Press, Ellesmere.

- Forbes, David Carl. (1966). *Small Stream Fishing*. George Newnes Ltd, London.

- Marshall Hardy, E. (1942). *Coarse Fish*. Herbert Jenkins, London.

- Houghton, MA, FLS, The Reverend W. (1879). *British Fresh-Water Fishes*. William Mackenzie, London. (Note: This book has been reprinted over the decades by numerous publishers, for example by the Peerage Press, London, in 1981.)

- Sheringham, Hugh Tempest. (1910). *An Open Creel*. Methuen and Co., London. (Republished in 1997 by the Medlar Press, Ellesmere.)

- Sheringham, Hugh Tempest and Studdy, G.E. (1925). *Fishing: Its Cause, Treatment and Cure*. Philip Allan and Co.

- Venables, Bernard. (1962). *Mr Crabtree Goes Fishing*. Daily Mirror, London.

- Walton, Izaak and Cotton, Charles. (1653). *The Compleat Angler*. Maurice Clark, London. (Available these days in many editions and publishers).

- Willughby, Francis. (1686). *Willughby de Piscibus. Historia Piscium*. Oxford. (This is a very rare and delicate book. The Freshwater Biological Association holds a copy.)

- Wilson, John and Turnbull, Chris. (1993). *The Anglers Guide To Freshwater Fish*. Boxtree Ltd. ISBN 1 85283 412 9.

- Winfield, Ian J. and Nelson, J.S. (Eds.) (1991). *Cyprinid Fishes: Systematics, Biology and Exploitation*. Chapman and Hall, London and New York.

- Yates, Chris. (2006). *How to fish*. Hamish Hamilton Ltd.

Some of these books need no further words of introduction. Others might just interest you. There are many more, some good and others poor, and doubtless others that are lost gems just waiting somewhere on a dusty bookshelf for you or me to rediscover them!

Other references used in researching this volume

I have made use of, and sometimes referenced too, various additional books and publications in preparing this work on the dace. A subset of the more prominent of these includes:

- 'A Regular Rod'. (2006). Derbyshire Diary. *Waterlog*, No.58, Winter 2006, pp.85-87.

- Alabaster, J.S. and Lloyd, R. (1980). *Water Quality Criteria for Freshwater Fish*. Butterworths, London.

- Ashley-Cooper, John. (1985). *A Ring of Wessex Water*. H.F and G. Witherby Ltd, London.

- Bucknall, Geoffrey. (1968). *Fly-fishing Tactics on Rivers*. Frederick Muller Ltd, London.

- Clower, Kenneth W. (1962). *Fishing Famous Rivers: Hampshire Avon*. Angling Times Books.

- Edwards, Ron W. and Brooker, M.P. (1982). *The Ecology of the Wye*. Dr W. Junk Publishers, London.

- Giles, Nick. (1994). *Freshwater Fish of the British Isles: A Guide for Anglers and Naturalists*. Swan Hill Press, Shrewsbury.

- Giles, Nick. (2005). *The Nature of Trout*. Perca Press, Verwood.

- Howes, William J. (1959). *Fly-fishing for Coarse Fish*. Herbert Jenkins, London.

- Marshall-Hardy, Eric. (1936). *Angling Yarns*. Herbert Jenkins, London.

- Martin, J.W. (the 'Trent Otter'). (1908). *My Fishing Days and Fishing Ways*. (Re-published by the Medlar Press, Ellsesmere.)

- McParlin, Pete. (2007). The coarse of the stream. *Waterlog*, 61, pp.80-84.

- Mills, Derek. (2005). Dainty dace. *Waterlog*, 50, pp.12-13.

- Muus, Bent J. and Dahlstrom, Preben. (1971). *Collins Guide to the Freshwater Fishes of Britain and Europe*. Collins, London.

- Pinder, Adrian C. (2001). *Keys to Larval and Juvenile Stages of Coarse Fishes from Fresh Waters in the British Isles*. The Freshwater Biological Association, Scientific Publication No.60, Windermere.

- River Restoration Centre. (1999). *The River Restoration Centre Manual of River Restoration Techniques*. River Restoration Centre, Silsoe.

- Tate Regan, C. (1911). *The Freshwater Fishes of the British Isles*. Methuen and Co. Ltd., London.

- Thomas, Henry Sullivan. (1873). *The Rod in India*. (Reprinted by The Naval and Military Press Ltd., Uckfield, East Sussex.)

- Venables, Bernard. (1993). *The Illustrated Memoirs of a Fisherman*. Merlin Unwin, Ludlow.

- Wild Trout Trust. (2006). *The Wild Trout Survival Guide*. The Wild Trout Trust, Waterlooville.

- Walker, Richard S. (1955). *Stillwater Angling*. (Second Edition). Macgibbon and Kee, London.

- Weatherley, Neil S. (1987). The diet and growth of 0-group dace, *Leuciscus leuciscus* (L.),and roach, *Rutilus rutilus* (L.), in a lowland river. *Journal of Fish Biology*, 30, pp.237-247.

Online sources

For those who are comfortable with computers as well as paper, FISHBASE is an invaluable website containing an authoritative international repository of vetted biological information about fish species. Go to wwwfishbase.org for info on dace, dobule, graining, or indeed any other fish species of interest.

A final word on dace and angling literature

In his Foreword to Eric Marshall-Hardy's 1936 book *Angling Yarns*, His Grace the Duke of Rutland wrote that:

> *"It has been said that hours spent fishing are not deducted from a man's allotted span. This may account for the ripe old age of many devotees of the sport. It is to be hoped that hours spent reading angling literature will be similarly discounted, for there can be no sport about which more has been written."*

Let us hope that this is true and that this bibliography and my own modest contribution through this book increase your health and longevity!

Dace fiction

As I thumb through my old fishing books and reflect back on angling magazines of yesterday, I can think of a few – written before the modern 'instruction book' days we now inhabit – where dace were part of the river scenery of a good tale. However, can I think of a story where the dace takes centre stage? The answer is short; albeit not quite as short as the story list itself!

I have got a little excited in the descriptions of big dace captures throughout this book. However, since they are neither fiction nor really traditional 'stories', they don't count as 'true' dace fiction. So, when I looked at my own hefty back-catalogue of angling fiction – published variously in angling magazines most significantly including a long series in *Waterlog* or else in my short story anthologies that have been ready for publication for some years and the many more tales I have written that currently lack a home – I realised that I was as guilty as the next angling author of overlooking a fish that I hold in high esteem. It is with this in mind that I have written one: *In pursuit of the prince*. Enjoy!

In pursuit of the prince

In those precious hours that were not dominated by work, family, shopping or commuting, there was just one thing occupying my angling brain.

The Pursuit of the Prince!

The *Prince of the Stream*, as I call it, is one of the most elegant fish that swims in any water on this planet. Dace, otherwise known as 'dart' or 'dare' depending upon from where one hails, have a unique beauty. Each is a bar of pure platinum, sprightly and nimble in the sharper flows of major rivers and smaller streams alike.

Yet they are overlooked by many, spurned by a number or, yet more ignominiously, regarded merely as pike bait to be lugged unceremoniously and illegally in buckets to aid the hunt for a predatory leviathan. The respect with which some amongst our angling kin hold this dainty fish is hardly commensurate with the elegant status of this *Prince of the Stream*.

And yet, for folk like me, folk perhaps slightly touched by the moon, the Prince is a special fish. Even the most modest is a thing of beauty. A big one, above the magical one-pound barrier, is as noble and challenging a quest as that for a two-pound roach or a thirty-pound pike. So what that one's muscles are not strained by cradling a specimen?

And so I sat and plotted, hot mug of tea cupped in my hands, gazing out of the window whilst considering where the plumpest of dace would now be lying.

Now was the magic, late-season time of year, as the dace were about to spawn. The male fish were rough to the touch with the growth of fine tubercles across their bodies. The female fish were swollen in the belly, as soft and laden with roe as fat herrings. The fish shoaled densely, in readiness any time soon to mingle spawn and milt over riffle-flushed shingle.

The chance of a pound-plus specimen was at its peak now, though the achievement of such a lofty goal was far from certain. Finding them was the first hurdle. Offering food that they would recognise, and then providing sufficient delicacy of presentation in the shallow, clear waters, were further steps then to be surmounted. And then, as likely as not, one would have to contend with a fat chub interloping with the shoal, muscling its way to the bait first, then erupting in the shallows to send the wary dace skittering for cover.

As I pondered such leuciscine matters, I gazed out of the window across our back garden, admiring the view. I am, in truth, no gardener. It is always my better half who first suffers sufficient pangs of guilt to break out the lawnmower and tame the jungle outside at some indeterminate point late each spring. However, I was the prime mover in the buying this house, and it was the garden that seduced me.

Our garden is not a huge tract of land, and neither is the landscape dramatic. It was not the once-neat lawn, nor the formerly tidily-clipped shrubs and orderly flower beds that caught my attention. No, useful source of worms though each of them could be, it was the edge of the garden that had called to me, then as now. For – joy of joys! – the margin of our land was defined by a chattering stream, barely inches deep and narrow enough to jump right across in places, yet alive with invertebrates, bullheads, loaches and small birds. A man who loves water should live by water, or so it seemed to me. We had to have this house, despite the relative inconvenience of its location for school and public transport and the warnings of insurance agents about the likelihood of flooding!

And so now I peered out of the window, lost in my reverie of giant dace, caught by the glint of water as the winter sun peeked in low through the barren scrub on the opposite bank. Yes, dace fishing it would be this afternoon, but where would I find myself that mercurial prize?

As the mug of tea cooled in my hands, I formulated a plan of attack. Where the two headwaters of the main river joined, they formed an alluring pool with both fast and slow water juxtaposed. And there, I had come to know, the dace would mass by day, the deeper water covering their backs, before the nocturnal run to the shallow shingles upstream on both tributaries. My mind was set and, partner and daughter off shopping, the remains of the afternoon were available to me to act upon that decision.

Setting down my mug in the kitchen, I prepared my tackle and donned warm clothes against the frost that had endured all day in the shade. No day for roach this. No, today was about the *Pursuit of the Prince*!

In no time at all, I had parked the car, shouldered the kit, and was trudging across the meadow, the grass still crisp underfoot. Under the weight of my seat and tackle bags, I was sweating slightly in spite of the chilly day. However, I was all too aware that the cold would infiltrate any chink in my defences as, later on, I worked the float or else sat hawk-like for the tiniest jerk or drop-back of my quivertip.

Like the effervescent fight of a big dace, I was all of a quiver inside with the anticipation of sport as I set the tackle up. I readied just two rods for action on this short, late-afternoon session: a light waggler, in preference to the stick float, for some upstream casting, and a delicate quiver that would fare me well as the light ebbed from the sky. With catapult and red maggots prepared, I sat low to the horizon in my seat.

I fired several small volleys of maggots upstream into the fast run of the larger tributary stream, an appetiser to whet the hunger of the specimens that I just knew, or perhaps just hoped hard enough to convince myself, would be lurking there. This I carried on doing for perhaps ten minutes, whilst any disturbance I might have made on my arrival was forgotten and, seated low to the horizon, I had melded with the scenery. I have found this attention to one's concealment so important over the years on these small rivers, and particularly so when they as low and clear as they now were in the late winter. Really big dace may be a high aspiration, but they rapidly become an impossible dream when they know you are there!

And then I cast, a gentle underhand flick upstream to where the sharp current entered the pool, the pair of red maggots sinking naturally with the turbulent flow. I held the rod tip as high as I could within the constraint of the canopy of willow twigs overhanging the pool, trying to keep the current from clutching and dragging on any slack line. The waggler righted and settled, the bait falling unimpeded through the clear waters to trundle the shallow run. It ran the pool's length with not so much as a tremor, before then pulling under as the hook snared the bed where the pool shallowed up towards its tail.

Another small pouch of perhaps half-a-dozen red maggots and another gentle flick, and the waggler was riding the stream again. However, this time, it buried emphatically as soon as it reached the drop-off into darker water.

I twisted my wrist gently to tighten into lively resistance, swinging the rod immediately low to my left to prevent the fish from 'exploding' on the surface. Patiently, I led the twisting fish towards my feet and the waiting landing net.

At around six ounces, this was a handsome dace, shimmering bright silver against the dark mesh in the slanting rays of the sun. I slipped the hook, appreciating its simple, elegant lines, before sliding it back into the cool current. It vanished instantly with a flick of the tail, darting off to rejoin its shoal-mates.

I waited again, hoping that I had not scared the remaining fish in the shallow, bright waters, flicking out just a few maggots at intervals to reassure and tempt the shoal.

As I sat intent upon the river, a sharp two-note call rang out from beyond my line of sight down the river. I froze instinctively as the brilliant azure of a kingfisher swept up the stream, low to the dancing surface, to settle on an overhanging willow bough opposite. It could have been perching no more than thirty feet from where I sat, yet my immobility had rendered me as invisible or irrelevant to the bird as the straggling dead rush stems still oscillating with the flow. There sat the kingfisher, his amber underside now adding rich warmth to the cool colours of the winter river. And then he was off again, a gaudy arrow spearing upstream, leaving no more than a waver of the willow branch as evidence of his passing.

In five more minutes, I cast again, the waggler arcing across the pool and landing with a gentle splash at the head of the run. The float once again righted itself and sank to a dot, gyrating with the current as it entered the deeper waters of the pool. I mended the line to avoid unnatural drag on the float's path, winding back the slack as the peacock quill traversed the pool towards me.

Another fruitless trot, perhaps this time indicating a frightened or, even worse, a vanished shoal? Or perhaps I had just to bide my time and be patient whilst the dace found my bait in the glacial, energy-sapping water?

The next trot down answered my questions as a fat female fish, plump with roe, fought bravely across the pool against the lightly-applied yet overwhelming force of my light tackle. Soon, she was mine, nestled in the folds of my net, where I slipped the hook without lifting her from the water in order to avoid additional stresses on her spawn-filled body.

Can a fish get more beautiful? All platinum with bronze highlights, she mouthed water whilst I sneaked a moment's glance before allowing her to fin back in readiness to shed her eggs in the near future.

And so the remaining afternoon passed, a pleasant and all-too-brief sojourn punctuated only periodically with dace and yet pervaded by the consistent delight of a river irrepressibly alive in the dead time of winter.

I did not set up the quivertip to see out the dusk. Like a rare sane person at a party, I knew that I had already drunk in my fill. And, anyhow, my conscience was telling me that the dace had best be left in peace with the stresses of spawning so very soon ahead.

As I paced the dark meadow on my way back to the car for the short ride home, I reflected on what a fine afternoon's sport it had been. I had not accumulated a huge bag of fish, nor indeed put out the keepnet at all with the fish in their more vulnerable, pre-spawning condition. Neither had I quite found the heavyweight dace that had swum in my imagination these days past.

Well, so be it; who could sneeze at such a handsome clutch of fish to twelve ounces or so, snatched from a frost-cleared winter river?

On this I reflected as we shared a family dinner on my return home, and later as I put my daughter to bed. Another day maybe? Or perhaps another year, given the shortness of the days, the rapid progression of time, and the competing demands upon it from work, family and roach fishing?

But my mind nagged me still. Were I to get just one more chance, where might I find that special dace? If there was a true lunker lurking in my vicinity, where might it now be, backing up into the sharper flows and shallower waters as the urge to spawn overwhelmed it?

Before locking up the house prior to bedtime, I took my customary walk down to the edge of the stream that bounded our garden. Below, the music of water on shingle played its seductive lullaby. Above, the stars shone brightly against a velvet sky clarified by the frost that now misted my breath.

Where indeed could I pursue a *Prince of the Stream* of outstanding dimensions? I had given the confluence my best shot today, and in previous weeks I had tried out a number of other weir pools and fast runs with some success but without the ultimate prize.

Maybe it was just not going to happen for me this year?

Tired now, ready for sleep, I turned and walked back to the house, locking the door and turning out the kitchen lights before retiring upstairs to join the missus in bed.

In the tiny rivulet that bordered our garden, the great female dace, a true veteran at ten years old now and laden with spawn, registered the blinking out of a light as she finned upstream with her shoal. Tonight she would feed, the urge to spawn pulling her up into the shallowest and seemingly most insignificant of waters to seek nourishment and then to shed her roe. Mighty she was against her smaller shoal-mates, older and fattened with several thousand eggs which only a really exceptional specimen is able to carry.

She worked the stream's bed for invertebrates, ravenous now as the impending rigours of spawning made growing demands upon her body.

A stressful time it would be. But here, at least, there was no angler to disturb her.

Tomorrow's stories

It is to our own great loss that we forget the small things. Small compliments, small 'thank yous', small details in our work and leisure, and the myriad small things of nature that keep whole ecosystems vibrant and healthy. Though mightier in stature than a minnow or bleak, dace are still small fishes of the river. In fact, they are the smallest regularly angled-for species in our rivers and the smallest fish NOT to be blighted with the patronizing human description of 'minor' or 'lesser' species.

If there is just one pearl to offer you in this whole book, it is to appreciate and cherish the small things. Without them, the world cannot go on, and will certainly be too sick to sustain the big things like chub, pike, elephants, you and me. Dace, like bacteria, sticklebacks, aphids, fungi, grass and caddis, are the cogs that keep the wondrously complex and balanced machine of nature ticking along sustainably.

There should, in truth, be a wealth of dace fiction; perhaps we can help redress this oversight when we next meet on a long, dark evening in the village pub to talk of fish and the riverside?

Dace: The Prince of the Stream

DATE _____
LAUNCHING SITE _____
_____

TIDE _____
WIND _____
OCEAN/MARINE/SURF/BUOY _____
_____

PADDLE INFO _____
PADDLE PARTNERS _____
_____

TRIP GOALS _____
_____

ESTIMATED MILEAGE _____

NOTES

_____
_____
_____
_____
_____
_____
_____
_____
_____
_____
_____
_____
_____
_____
_____
_____
_____
_____
_____

DATE _____

LAUNCHING SITE _____

_____

TIDE _____

WIND _____

OCEAN/MARINE/SURF/BUOY _____

_____

PADDLE INFO _____

PADDLE PARTNERS _____

_____

TRIP GOALS _____

_____

ESTIMATED MILEAGE _____

NOTES

_____
_____
_____
_____
_____
_____
_____
_____
_____
_____
_____
_____
_____
_____
_____
_____
_____
_____
_____

DATE _____
LAUNCHING SITE _____
_____
TIDE _____
WIND _____
OCEAN/MARINE/SURF/BUOY _____
_____
PADDLE INFO _____
PADDLE PARTNERS _____
_____
TRIP GOALS _____
_____
ESTIMATED MILEAGE _____

NOTES

3

DATE _____

LAUNCHING SITE _____

_____

TIDE _____

WIND _____

OCEAN/MARINE/SURF/BUOY _____

_____

PADDLE INFO _____

PADDLE PARTNERS _____

_____

TRIP GOALS _____

_____

ESTIMATED MILEAGE _____

NOTES

_____
_____
_____
_____
_____
_____
_____
_____
_____
_____
_____
_____
_____
_____
_____
_____
_____
_____
_____

DATE _____

LAUNCHING SITE _____

TIDE _____

WIND _____

OCEAN/MARINE/SURF/BUOY _____

PADDLE INFO _____

PADDLE PARTNERS _____

TRIP GOALS _____

ESTIMATED MILEAGE _____

NOTES

_____
_____
_____
_____
_____
_____
_____
_____
_____
_____
_____
_____
_____
_____
_____
_____
_____
_____
_____
_____
_____
_____
_____

DATE _____

LAUNCHING SITE _____

_____

TIDE _____

WIND _____

OCEAN/MARINE/SURF/BUOY _____

_____

PADDLE INFO _____

PADDLE PARTNERS _____

_____

TRIP GOALS _____

_____

ESTIMATED MILEAGE _____

NOTES

6

DATE _____

LAUNCHING SITE _____

_____

TIDE _____

WIND _____

OCEAN/MARINE/SURF/BUOY _____

_____

PADDLE INFO _____

PADDLE PARTNERS _____

_____

TRIP GOALS _____

_____

ESTIMATED MILEAGE _____

NOTES

_____
_____
_____
_____
_____
_____
_____
_____
_____
_____
_____
_____
_____
_____
_____
_____
_____
_____
_____

DATE _____

LAUNCHING SITE _____

_____

TIDE _____

WIND _____

OCEAN/MARINE/SURF/BUOY _____

_____

PADDLE INFO _____

PADDLE PARTNERS _____

_____

TRIP GOALS _____

_____

ESTIMATED MILEAGE _____

NOTES

_____

_____

_____

_____

_____

_____

_____

_____

_____

_____

_____

_____

_____

_____

_____

_____

_____

_____

DATE _____

LAUNCHING SITE _____

TIDE _____

WIND _____

OCEAN/MARINE/SURF/BUOY _____

PADDLE INFO _____

PADDLE PARTNERS _____

TRIP GOALS _____

ESTIMATED MILEAGE _____

NOTES

_____

_____

_____

_____

_____

_____

_____

_____

_____

_____

_____

_____

_____

_____

_____

_____

_____

_____

_____

_____

DATE _____

LAUNCHING SITE _____

_____

TIDE _____

WIND _____

OCEAN/MARINE/SURF/BUOY _____

_____

PADDLE INFO _____

PADDLE PARTNERS _____

_____

TRIP GOALS _____

_____

ESTIMATED MILEAGE _____

NOTES

_____
_____
_____
_____
_____
_____
_____
_____
_____
_____
_____
_____
_____
_____
_____
_____
_____
_____
_____

DATE _____

LAUNCHING SITE _____

_____

TIDE _____

WIND _____

OCEAN/MARINE/SURF/BUOY _____

_____

PADDLE INFO _____

PADDLE PARTNERS _____

_____

TRIP GOALS _____

_____

ESTIMATED MILEAGE _____

NOTES

_____
_____
_____
_____
_____
_____
_____
_____
_____
_____
_____
_____
_____
_____
_____
_____
_____
_____
_____
_____
_____

DATE _____
LAUNCHING SITE _____
_____
TIDE _____
WIND _____
OCEAN/MARINE/SURF/BUOY _____
_____
PADDLE INFO _____
PADDLE PARTNERS _____
_____
TRIP GOALS _____
_____
ESTIMATED MILEAGE _____

NOTES

DATE _____

LAUNCHING SITE _____

TIDE _____

WIND _____

OCEAN/MARINE/SURF/BUOY _____

PADDLE INFO _____

PADDLE PARTNERS _____

TRIP GOALS _____

ESTIMATED MILEAGE _____

NOTES

_____
_____
_____
_____
_____
_____
_____
_____
_____
_____
_____
_____
_____
_____
_____
_____
_____
_____
_____
_____

DATE _____

LAUNCHING SITE _____

_____

TIDE _____

WIND _____

OCEAN/MARINE/SURF/BUOY _____

_____

PADDLE INFO _____

PADDLE PARTNERS _____

_____

TRIP GOALS _____

_____

ESTIMATED MILEAGE _____

NOTES

_____
_____
_____
_____
_____
_____
_____
_____
_____
_____
_____
_____
_____
_____
_____
_____
_____
_____
_____

DATE _____

LAUNCHING SITE _____

TIDE _____

WIND _____

OCEAN/MARINE/SURF/BUOY _____

PADDLE INFO _____

PADDLE PARTNERS _____

TRIP GOALS _____

ESTIMATED MILEAGE _____

NOTES

_____
_____
_____
_____
_____
_____
_____
_____
_____
_____
_____
_____
_____
_____
_____
_____
_____
_____

DATE _____

LAUNCHING SITE _____

_____

TIDE _____

WIND _____

OCEAN/MARINE/SURF/BUOY _____

_____

PADDLE INFO _____

PADDLE PARTNERS _____

_____

TRIP GOALS _____

_____

ESTIMATED MILEAGE _____

NOTES

_____
_____
_____
_____
_____
_____
_____
_____
_____
_____
_____
_____
_____
_____
_____
_____
_____
_____

DATE _____

LAUNCHING SITE _____

TIDE _____

WIND _____

OCEAN/MARINE/SURF/BUOY _____

PADDLE INFO _____

PADDLE PARTNERS _____

TRIP GOALS _____

ESTIMATED MILEAGE _____

NOTES

_____

_____

_____

_____

_____

_____

_____

_____

_____

_____

_____

_____

_____

_____

_____

_____

_____

_____

_____

DATE _____

LAUNCHING SITE _____

_____

TIDE _____

WIND _____

OCEAN/MARINE/SURF/BUOY _____

_____

PADDLE INFO _____

PADDLE PARTNERS _____

_____

TRIP GOALS _____

_____

ESTIMATED MILEAGE _____

NOTES

DATE _____

LAUNCHING SITE _____

_____

TIDE _____

WIND _____

OCEAN/MARINE/SURF/BUOY _____

_____

PADDLE INFO _____

PADDLE PARTNERS _____

_____

TRIP GOALS _____

_____

ESTIMATED MILEAGE _____

NOTES

_____
_____
_____
_____
_____
_____
_____
_____
_____
_____
_____
_____
_____
_____
_____
_____
_____
_____

DATE _____

LAUNCHING SITE _____

_____

TIDE _____

WIND _____

OCEAN/MARINE/SURF/BUOY _____

_____

PADDLE INFO _____

PADDLE PARTNERS _____

_____

TRIP GOALS _____

_____

ESTIMATED MILEAGE _____

NOTES

_____

_____

_____

_____

_____

_____

_____

_____

_____

_____

_____

_____

_____

_____

_____

_____

_____

_____

_____

DATE _____

LAUNCHING SITE _____

_____

TIDE _____

WIND _____

OCEAN/MARINE/SURF/BUOY _____

_____

PADDLE INFO _____

PADDLE PARTNERS _____

_____

TRIP GOALS _____

_____

ESTIMATED MILEAGE _____

NOTES

_____
_____
_____
_____
_____
_____
_____
_____
_____
_____
_____
_____
_____
_____
_____
_____
_____
_____
_____
_____
_____

DATE _____

LAUNCHING SITE _____

_____

TIDE _____

WIND _____

OCEAN/MARINE/SURF/BUOY _____

_____

PADDLE INFO _____

PADDLE PARTNERS _____

_____

TRIP GOALS _____

_____

ESTIMATED MILEAGE _____

NOTES

_____

_____

_____

_____

_____

_____

_____

_____

_____

_____

_____

_____

_____

_____

_____

_____

_____

_____

DATE _____

LAUNCHING SITE _____

TIDE _____

WIND _____

OCEAN/MARINE/SURF/BUOY _____

PADDLE INFO _____

PADDLE PARTNERS _____

TRIP GOALS _____

ESTIMATED MILEAGE _____

NOTES

_____
_____
_____
_____
_____
_____
_____
_____
_____
_____
_____
_____
_____
_____
_____
_____
_____
_____
_____

DATE _____

LAUNCHING SITE _____

_____

TIDE _____

WIND _____

OCEAN/MARINE/SURF/BUOY _____

_____

PADDLE INFO _____

PADDLE PARTNERS _____

_____

TRIP GOALS _____

_____

ESTIMATED MILEAGE _____

NOTES

DATE _____

LAUNCHING SITE _____

_____

TIDE _____

WIND _____

OCEAN/MARINE/SURF/BUOY _____

_____

PADDLE INFO _____

PADDLE PARTNERS _____

_____

TRIP GOALS _____

_____

ESTIMATED MILEAGE _____

NOTES

_____
_____
_____
_____
_____
_____
_____
_____
_____
_____
_____
_____
_____
_____
_____
_____
_____
_____
_____

DATE _____

LAUNCHING SITE _____

_____

TIDE _____

WIND _____

OCEAN/MARINE/SURF/BUOY _____

_____

PADDLE INFO _____

PADDLE PARTNERS _____

_____

TRIP GOALS _____

_____

ESTIMATED MILEAGE _____

NOTES

_____
_____
_____
_____
_____
_____
_____
_____
_____
_____
_____
_____
_____
_____
_____
_____
_____
_____
_____

DATE _____
LAUNCHING SITE _____
_____
TIDE _____
WIND _____
OCEAN/MARINE/SURF/BUOY _____
_____
PADDLE INFO _____
PADDLE PARTNERS _____
_____
TRIP GOALS _____
_____
ESTIMATED MILEAGE _____

NOTES

_____
_____
_____
_____
_____
_____
_____
_____
_____
_____
_____
_____
_____
_____
_____
_____
_____
_____
_____
_____

DATE _____

LAUNCHING SITE _____

_____

TIDE _____

WIND _____

OCEAN/MARINE/SURF/BUOY _____

_____

PADDLE INFO _____

PADDLE PARTNERS _____

_____

TRIP GOALS _____

_____

ESTIMATED MILEAGE _____

NOTES

_____
_____
_____
_____
_____
_____
_____
_____
_____
_____
_____
_____
_____
_____
_____
_____
_____
_____

DATE _____
LAUNCHING SITE _____

TIDE _____
WIND _____
OCEAN/MARINE/SURF/BUOY _____

PADDLE INFO _____
PADDLE PARTNERS _____

TRIP GOALS _____

ESTIMATED MILEAGE _____

NOTES

_____
_____
_____
_____
_____
_____
_____
_____
_____
_____
_____
_____
_____
_____
_____
_____
_____
_____

29

DATE _____

LAUNCHING SITE _____

_____

TIDE _____

WIND _____

OCEAN/MARINE/SURF/BUOY _____

_____

PADDLE INFO _____

PADDLE PARTNERS _____

_____

TRIP GOALS _____

_____

ESTIMATED MILEAGE _____

NOTES

DATE _____

LAUNCHING SITE _____

_____

TIDE _____

WIND _____

OCEAN/MARINE/SURF/BUOY _____

_____

PADDLE INFO _____

PADDLE PARTNERS _____

_____

TRIP GOALS _____

_____

ESTIMATED MILEAGE _____

NOTES

DATE _____

LAUNCHING SITE _____

_____

TIDE _____

WIND _____

OCEAN/MARINE/SURF/BUOY _____

_____

PADDLE INFO _____

PADDLE PARTNERS _____

_____

TRIP GOALS _____

_____

ESTIMATED MILEAGE _____

NOTES

_____
_____
_____
_____
_____
_____
_____
_____
_____
_____
_____
_____
_____
_____
_____
_____
_____
_____
_____
_____

DATE _____

LAUNCHING SITE _____

TIDE _____

WIND _____

OCEAN/MARINE/SURF/BUOY _____

PADDLE INFO _____

PADDLE PARTNERS _____

TRIP GOALS _____

ESTIMATED MILEAGE _____

NOTES

_____
_____
_____
_____
_____
_____
_____
_____
_____
_____
_____
_____
_____
_____
_____
_____
_____
_____
_____

DATE _____

LAUNCHING SITE _____

_____

TIDE _____

WIND _____

OCEAN/MARINE/SURF/BUOY _____

_____

PADDLE INFO _____

PADDLE PARTNERS _____

_____

TRIP GOALS _____

_____

ESTIMATED MILEAGE _____

NOTES

_____
_____
_____
_____
_____
_____
_____
_____
_____
_____
_____
_____
_____
_____
_____
_____
_____
_____
_____

_____
_____
_____

DATE _____

LAUNCHING SITE _____

_____

TIDE _____

WIND _____

OCEAN/MARINE/SURF/BUOY _____

_____

PADDLE INFO _____

PADDLE PARTNERS _____

_____

TRIP GOALS _____

_____

ESTIMATED MILEAGE _____

NOTES

_____
_____
_____
_____
_____
_____
_____
_____
_____
_____
_____
_____
_____
_____
_____
_____
_____

DATE _____

LAUNCHING SITE _____

_____

TIDE _____

WIND _____

OCEAN/MARINE/SURF/BUOY _____

_____

PADDLE INFO _____

PADDLE PARTNERS _____

_____

TRIP GOALS _____

_____

ESTIMATED MILEAGE _____

NOTES

_____
_____
_____
_____
_____
_____
_____
_____
_____
_____
_____
_____
_____
_____
_____
_____
_____
_____
_____
_____

DATE _____

LAUNCHING SITE _____

_____

TIDE _____

WIND _____

OCEAN/MARINE/SURF/BUOY _____

_____

PADDLE INFO _____

PADDLE PARTNERS _____

_____

TRIP GOALS _____

_____

ESTIMATED MILEAGE _____

NOTES

_____
_____
_____
_____
_____
_____
_____
_____
_____
_____
_____
_____
_____
_____
_____
_____
_____
_____
_____

DATE _____

LAUNCHING SITE _____

_____

TIDE _____

WIND _____

OCEAN/MARINE/SURF/BUOY _____

_____

PADDLE INFO _____

PADDLE PARTNERS _____

_____

TRIP GOALS _____

_____

ESTIMATED MILEAGE _____

NOTES

_____
_____
_____
_____
_____
_____
_____
_____
_____
_____
_____
_____
_____
_____
_____
_____
_____

DATE _____
LAUNCHING SITE _____

TIDE _____
WIND _____
OCEAN/MARINE/SURF/BUOY _____

PADDLE INFO _____
PADDLE PARTNERS _____

TRIP GOALS _____

ESTIMATED MILEAGE _____

NOTES

_____
_____
_____
_____
_____
_____
_____
_____
_____
_____
_____
_____
_____
_____
_____
_____
_____
_____
_____
_____

DATE _____

LAUNCHING SITE _____

_____

TIDE _____

WIND _____

OCEAN/MARINE/SURF/BUOY _____

_____

PADDLE INFO _____

PADDLE PARTNERS _____

_____

TRIP GOALS _____

_____

ESTIMATED MILEAGE _____

NOTES

DATE _____

LAUNCHING SITE _____

TIDE _____

WIND _____

OCEAN/MARINE/SURF/BUOY _____

PADDLE INFO _____

PADDLE PARTNERS _____

TRIP GOALS _____

ESTIMATED MILEAGE _____

NOTES

_____
_____
_____
_____
_____
_____
_____
_____
_____
_____
_____
_____
_____
_____
_____
_____
_____
_____
_____
_____

DATE _____

LAUNCHING SITE _____

_____

TIDE _____

WIND _____

OCEAN/MARINE/SURF/BUOY _____

_____

PADDLE INFO _____

PADDLE PARTNERS _____

_____

TRIP GOALS _____

_____

ESTIMATED MILEAGE _____

NOTES

_____
_____
_____
_____
_____
_____
_____
_____
_____
_____
_____
_____
_____
_____
_____
_____
_____

DATE _____

LAUNCHING SITE _____

_____

TIDE _____

WIND _____

OCEAN/MARINE/SURF/BUOY _____

_____

PADDLE INFO _____

PADDLE PARTNERS _____

_____

TRIP GOALS _____

_____

ESTIMATED MILEAGE _____

NOTES

_____
_____
_____
_____
_____
_____
_____
_____
_____
_____
_____
_____
_____
_____
_____
_____
_____
_____

_____

_____

_____

DATE _____

LAUNCHING SITE _____

_____

TIDE _____

WIND _____

OCEAN/MARINE/SURF/BUOY _____

_____

PADDLE INFO _____

PADDLE PARTNERS _____

_____

TRIP GOALS _____

_____

ESTIMATED MILEAGE _____

NOTES

_____
_____
_____
_____
_____
_____
_____
_____
_____
_____
_____
_____
_____
_____
_____
_____
_____
_____

DATE _____
LAUNCHING SITE _____

TIDE _____
WIND _____
OCEAN/MARINE/SURF/BUOY _____

PADDLE INFO _____
PADDLE PARTNERS _____

TRIP GOALS _____

ESTIMATED MILEAGE _____

NOTES

_____
_____
_____
_____
_____
_____
_____
_____
_____
_____
_____
_____
_____
_____
_____
_____
_____
_____
_____

DATE _____

LAUNCHING SITE _____

_____

TIDE _____

WIND _____

OCEAN/MARINE/SURF/BUOY _____

_____

PADDLE INFO _____

PADDLE PARTNERS _____

_____

TRIP GOALS _____

_____

ESTIMATED MILEAGE _____

NOTES

_____

_____

_____

_____

_____

_____

_____

_____

_____

_____

_____

_____

_____

_____

_____

_____

_____

_____

_____

_____

_____

ATE _____

AUNCHING SITE _____

_____

DE _____

VIND _____

CEAN/MARINE/SURF/BUOY _____

_____

ADDLE INFO _____

ADDLE PARTNERS _____

_____

RIP GOALS _____

_____

STIMATED MILEAGE _____

NOTES

DATE _____

LAUNCHING SITE _____

_____

TIDE _____

WIND _____

OCEAN/MARINE/SURF/BUOY _____

_____

PADDLE INFO _____

PADDLE PARTNERS _____

_____

TRIP GOALS _____

_____

ESTIMATED MILEAGE _____

NOTES

_____
_____
_____
_____
_____
_____
_____
_____
_____
_____
_____
_____
_____
_____
_____
_____
_____
_____
_____

DATE _____

LAUNCHING SITE _____
_____

TIDE _____

WIND _____

OCEAN/MARINE/SURF/BUOY _____
_____

PADDLE INFO _____

PADDLE PARTNERS _____
_____

TRIP GOALS _____
_____

ESTIMATED MILEAGE _____

NOTES

_____
_____
_____
_____
_____
_____
_____
_____
_____
_____
_____
_____
_____
_____
_____
_____
_____
_____

DATE _____

LAUNCHING SITE _____

_____

TIDE _____

WIND _____

OCEAN/MARINE/SURF/BUOY _____

_____

PADDLE INFO _____

PADDLE PARTNERS _____

_____

TRIP GOALS _____

_____

ESTIMATED MILEAGE _____

NOTES

_____
_____
_____
_____
_____
_____
_____
_____
_____
_____
_____
_____
_____
_____
_____
_____
_____
_____

DATE _____
LAUNCHING SITE _____
_____

TIDE _____
WIND _____
OCEAN/MARINE/SURF/BUOY _____
_____

PADDLE INFO _____
PADDLE PARTNERS _____
_____

TRIP GOALS _____
_____

ESTIMATED MILEAGE _____

NOTES

_____
_____
_____
_____
_____
_____
_____
_____
_____
_____
_____
_____
_____
_____
_____
_____
_____
_____
_____
_____
_____

DATE _____

LAUNCHING SITE _____

_____

TIDE _____

WIND _____

OCEAN/MARINE/SURF/BUOY _____

_____

PADDLE INFO _____

PADDLE PARTNERS _____

_____

TRIP GOALS _____

_____

ESTIMATED MILEAGE _____

NOTES

_____
_____
_____
_____
_____
_____
_____
_____
_____
_____
_____
_____
_____
_____
_____
_____
_____
_____

ATE _____

AUNCHING SITE _____
_____

DE _____

VIND _____

CEAN/MARINE/SURF/BUOY _____
_____

ADDLE INFO _____

ADDLE PARTNERS _____
_____

RIP GOALS _____
_____

STIMATED MILEAGE _____

NOTES

_____
_____
_____
_____
_____
_____
_____
_____
_____
_____
_____
_____
_____
_____
_____
_____
_____
_____
_____
_____
_____

DATE _____

LAUNCHING SITE _____

_____

TIDE _____

WIND _____

OCEAN/MARINE/SURF/BUOY _____

_____

PADDLE INFO _____

PADDLE PARTNERS _____

_____

TRIP GOALS _____

_____

ESTIMATED MILEAGE _____

NOTES

DATE _____

LAUNCHING SITE _____

TIDE _____

WIND _____

OCEAN/MARINE/SURF/BUOY _____

PADDLE INFO _____

PADDLE PARTNERS _____

TRIP GOALS _____

ESTIMATED MILEAGE _____

NOTES

_____

_____

_____

_____

_____

_____

_____

_____

_____

_____

_____

_____

_____

_____

_____

_____

_____

_____

_____

_____

DATE _____

LAUNCHING SITE _____

_____

TIDE _____

WIND _____

OCEAN/MARINE/SURF/BUOY _____

_____

PADDLE INFO _____

PADDLE PARTNERS _____

_____

TRIP GOALS _____

_____

ESTIMATED MILEAGE _____

NOTES

_____
_____
_____
_____
_____
_____
_____
_____
_____
_____
_____
_____
_____
_____
_____
_____
_____
_____
_____
_____

DATE _____

LAUNCHING SITE _____

_____

TIDE _____

WIND _____

OCEAN/MARINE/SURF/BUOY _____

_____

PADDLE INFO _____

PADDLE PARTNERS _____

_____

TRIP GOALS _____

_____

ESTIMATED MILEAGE _____

NOTES

DATE _____

LAUNCHING SITE _____

_____

TIDE _____

WIND _____

OCEAN/MARINE/SURF/BUOY _____

_____

PADDLE INFO _____

PADDLE PARTNERS _____

_____

TRIP GOALS _____

_____

ESTIMATED MILEAGE _____

NOTES

_____
_____
_____
_____
_____
_____
_____
_____
_____
_____
_____
_____
_____
_____
_____
_____
_____
_____
_____

ATE _____

AUNCHING SITE _____

DE _____

WIND _____

CEAN/MARINE/SURF/BUOY _____

ADDLE INFO _____

ADDLE PARTNERS _____

RIP GOALS _____

STIMATED MILEAGE _____

NOTES

_____
_____
_____
_____
_____
_____
_____
_____
_____
_____
_____
_____
_____
_____
_____
_____
_____
_____

DATE _____

LAUNCHING SITE _____

_____

TIDE _____

WIND _____

OCEAN/MARINE/SURF/BUOY _____

_____

PADDLE INFO _____

PADDLE PARTNERS _____

_____

TRIP GOALS _____

_____

ESTIMATED MILEAGE _____

NOTES

DATE _____

LAUNCHING SITE _____

TIDE _____

WIND _____

OCEAN/MARINE/SURF/BUOY _____

PADDLE INFO _____

PADDLE PARTNERS _____

TRIP GOALS _____

ESTIMATED MILEAGE _____

NOTES

_____
_____
_____
_____
_____
_____
_____
_____
_____
_____
_____
_____
_____
_____
_____
_____
_____
_____

DATE _____

LAUNCHING SITE _____

_____

TIDE _____

WIND _____

OCEAN/MARINE/SURF/BUOY _____

_____

PADDLE INFO _____

PADDLE PARTNERS _____

_____

TRIP GOALS _____

_____

ESTIMATED MILEAGE _____

NOTES

_____
_____
_____
_____
_____
_____
_____
_____
_____
_____
_____
_____
_____
_____
_____
_____
_____
_____
_____
_____

DATE _____

LAUNCHING SITE _____

TIDE _____

WIND _____

OCEAN/MARINE/SURF/BUOY _____

PADDLE INFO _____

PADDLE PARTNERS _____

TRIP GOALS _____

ESTIMATED MILEAGE _____

NOTES

_____
_____
_____
_____
_____
_____
_____
_____
_____
_____
_____
_____
_____
_____
_____
_____
_____
_____
_____
_____

DATE _____

LAUNCHING SITE _____

_____

TIDE _____

WIND _____

OCEAN/MARINE/SURF/BUOY _____

_____

PADDLE INFO _____

PADDLE PARTNERS _____

_____

TRIP GOALS _____

_____

ESTIMATED MILEAGE _____

NOTES

_____
_____
_____
_____
_____
_____
_____
_____
_____
_____
_____
_____
_____
_____
_____
_____
_____
_____
_____
_____

ATE _____

AUNCHING SITE _____

DE _____

IND _____

CEAN/MARINE/SURF/BUOY _____

ADDLE INFO _____

ADDLE PARTNERS _____

RIP GOALS _____

STIMATED MILEAGE _____

NOTES

DATE _____

LAUNCHING SITE _____
_____

TIDE _____

WIND _____

OCEAN/MARINE/SURF/BUOY _____
_____

PADDLE INFO _____

PADDLE PARTNERS _____
_____

TRIP GOALS _____
_____

ESTIMATED MILEAGE _____

NOTES

_____
_____
_____
_____
_____
_____
_____
_____
_____
_____
_____
_____
_____
_____
_____
_____
_____
_____
_____

DATE _____

LAUNCHING SITE _____

TIDE _____

WIND _____

OCEAN/MARINE/SURF/BUOY _____

PADDLE INFO _____

PADDLE PARTNERS _____

TRIP GOALS _____

ESTIMATED MILEAGE _____

NOTES

_____
_____
_____
_____
_____
_____
_____
_____
_____
_____
_____
_____
_____
_____
_____
_____
_____
_____
_____
_____

DATE _____

LAUNCHING SITE _____

_____

TIDE _____

WIND _____

OCEAN/MARINE/SURF/BUOY _____

_____

PADDLE INFO _____

PADDLE PARTNERS _____

_____

TRIP GOALS _____

_____

ESTIMATED MILEAGE _____

NOTES

_____
_____
_____
_____
_____
_____
_____
_____
_____
_____
_____
_____
_____
_____
_____
_____
_____

_____
_____
_____

DATE _____

LAUNCHING SITE _____

TIDE _____

WIND _____

OCEAN/MARINE/SURF/BUOY _____

PADDLE INFO _____

PADDLE PARTNERS _____

TRIP GOALS _____

ESTIMATED MILEAGE _____

NOTES

DATE _____

LAUNCHING SITE _____

_____

TIDE _____

WIND _____

OCEAN/MARINE/SURF/BUOY _____

_____

PADDLE INFO _____

PADDLE PARTNERS _____

_____

TRIP GOALS _____

_____

ESTIMATED MILEAGE _____

NOTES

_____
_____
_____
_____
_____
_____
_____
_____
_____
_____
_____
_____
_____
_____
_____
_____
_____
_____
_____

ATE _____

AUNCHING SITE _____

DE _____

IND _____

CEAN/MARINE/SURF/BUOY _____

ADDLE INFO _____

ADDLE PARTNERS _____

RIP GOALS _____

STIMATED MILEAGE _____

NOTES

DATE _____
LAUNCHING SITE _____

TIDE _____
WIND _____
OCEAN/MARINE/SURF/BUOY _____

PADDLE INFO _____
PADDLE PARTNERS _____

TRIP GOALS _____

ESTIMATED MILEAGE _____

NOTES

_____
_____
_____
_____
_____
_____
_____
_____
_____
_____
_____
_____
_____
_____
_____
_____
_____
_____

DATE _____

LAUNCHING SITE _____

_____

TIDE _____

WIND _____

OCEAN/MARINE/SURF/BUOY _____

_____

PADDLE INFO _____

PADDLE PARTNERS _____

_____

TRIP GOALS _____

_____

ESTIMATED MILEAGE _____

NOTES

_____
_____
_____
_____
_____
_____
_____
_____
_____
_____
_____
_____
_____
_____
_____
_____
_____
_____
_____

DATE _____

LAUNCHING SITE _____

_____

TIDE _____

WIND _____

OCEAN/MARINE/SURF/BUOY _____

_____

PADDLE INFO _____

PADDLE PARTNERS _____

_____

TRIP GOALS _____

_____

ESTIMATED MILEAGE _____

NOTES

_____
_____
_____
_____
_____
_____
_____
_____
_____
_____
_____
_____
_____
_____
_____
_____
_____
_____

_____

_____

_____

DATE _____

LAUNCHING SITE _____

TIDE _____

WIND _____

OCEAN/MARINE/SURF/BUOY _____

PADDLE INFO _____

PADDLE PARTNERS _____

TRIP GOALS _____

ESTIMATED MILEAGE _____

NOTES

_____
_____
_____
_____
_____
_____
_____
_____
_____
_____
_____
_____
_____
_____
_____
_____
_____

DATE _____

LAUNCHING SITE _____

_____

TIDE _____

WIND _____

OCEAN/MARINE/SURF/BUOY _____

PADDLE INFO _____

PADDLE PARTNERS _____

_____

TRIP GOALS _____

_____

ESTIMATED MILEAGE _____

NOTES

_____

_____

_____

_____

_____

_____

_____

_____

_____

_____

_____

_____

_____

_____

_____

_____

_____

_____

ATE _____

AUNCHING SITE _____

_____

DE _____

IND _____

CEAN/MARINE/SURF/BUOY _____

_____

ADDLE INFO _____

ADDLE PARTNERS _____

_____

RIP GOALS _____

_____

STIMATED MILEAGE _____

NOTES

_____

_____

_____

_____

_____

_____

_____

_____

_____

_____

_____

_____

_____

_____

_____

_____

_____

_____

_____

DATE _____

LAUNCHING SITE _____

_____

TIDE _____

WIND _____

OCEAN/MARINE/SURF/BUOY _____

_____

PADDLE INFO _____

PADDLE PARTNERS _____

_____

TRIP GOALS _____

_____

ESTIMATED MILEAGE _____

NOTES

_____

_____

_____

_____

_____

_____

_____

_____

_____

_____

_____

_____

_____

_____

_____

_____

_____

_____

DATE _____

LAUNCHING SITE _____

TIDE _____

WIND _____

OCEAN/MARINE/SURF/BUOY _____

PADDLE INFO _____

PADDLE PARTNERS _____

TRIP GOALS _____

ESTIMATED MILEAGE _____

NOTES

_____

_____

_____

_____

_____

_____

_____

_____

_____

_____

_____

_____

_____

_____

_____

_____

_____

_____

DATE _____

LAUNCHING SITE _____

_____

TIDE _____

WIND _____

OCEAN/MARINE/SURF/BUOY _____

_____

PADDLE INFO _____

PADDLE PARTNERS _____

_____

TRIP GOALS _____

_____

ESTIMATED MILEAGE _____

NOTES

ATE _____
AUNCHING SITE _____

IDE _____
VIND _____
CEAN/MARINE/SURF/BUOY _____

ADDLE INFO _____
ADDLE PARTNERS _____

RIP GOALS _____

STIMATED MILEAGE _____

NOTES

DATE _____

LAUNCHING SITE _____

_____

TIDE _____

WIND _____

OCEAN/MARINE/SURF/BUOY _____

_____

PADDLE INFO _____

PADDLE PARTNERS _____

_____

TRIP GOALS _____

_____

ESTIMATED MILEAGE _____

NOTES

_____
_____
_____
_____
_____
_____
_____
_____
_____
_____
_____
_____
_____
_____
_____
_____
_____
_____

ATE _____

AUNCHING SITE _____

_____

DE _____

IND _____

CEAN/MARINE/SURF/BUOY _____

_____

ADDLE INFO _____

ADDLE PARTNERS _____

_____

RIP GOALS _____

_____

STIMATED MILEAGE _____

NOTES

_____
_____
_____
_____
_____
_____
_____
_____
_____
_____
_____
_____
_____
_____
_____
_____
_____
_____
_____

DATE _____

LAUNCHING SITE _____

_____

TIDE _____

WIND _____

OCEAN/MARINE/SURF/BUOY _____

_____

PADDLE INFO _____

PADDLE PARTNERS _____

_____

TRIP GOALS _____

_____

ESTIMATED MILEAGE _____

NOTES

_____

_____

_____

_____

_____

_____

_____

_____

_____

_____

_____

_____

_____

_____

_____

_____

_____

_____

DATE _____

LAUNCHING SITE _____

TIDE _____

WIND _____

OCEAN/MARINE/SURF/BUOY _____

PADDLE INFO _____

PADDLE PARTNERS _____

TRIP GOALS _____

ESTIMATED MILEAGE _____

NOTES

DATE _____

LAUNCHING SITE _____

TIDE _____

WIND _____

OCEAN/MARINE/SURF/BUOY _____

PADDLE INFO _____

PADDLE PARTNERS _____

TRIP GOALS _____

ESTIMATED MILEAGE _____

NOTES

ATE _____

AUNCHING SITE _____
_____

DE _____

WIND _____

OCEAN/MARINE/SURF/BUOY _____
_____

PADDLE INFO _____

PADDLE PARTNERS _____
_____

TRIP GOALS _____
_____

ESTIMATED MILEAGE _____

NOTES

_____
_____
_____
_____
_____
_____
_____
_____
_____
_____
_____
_____
_____
_____
_____
_____
_____
_____
_____
_____
_____
_____

DATE _____

LAUNCHING SITE _____

_____

TIDE _____

WIND _____

OCEAN/MARINE/SURF/BUOY _____

_____

PADDLE INFO _____

PADDLE PARTNERS _____

_____

TRIP GOALS _____

_____

ESTIMATED MILEAGE _____

NOTES

_____
_____
_____
_____
_____
_____
_____
_____
_____
_____
_____
_____
_____
_____
_____
_____
_____
_____

ATE _____

AUNCHING SITE _____

_____

DE _____

IND _____

CEAN/MARINE/SURF/BUOY _____

_____

ADDLE INFO _____

ADDLE PARTNERS _____

_____

RIP GOALS _____

_____

STIMATED MILEAGE _____

NOTES

_____
_____
_____
_____
_____
_____
_____
_____
_____
_____
_____
_____
_____
_____
_____
_____
_____
_____
_____

DATE _____

LAUNCHING SITE _____

_____

TIDE _____

WIND _____

OCEAN/MARINE/SURF/BUOY _____

_____

PADDLE INFO _____

PADDLE PARTNERS _____

_____

TRIP GOALS _____

_____

ESTIMATED MILEAGE _____

NOTES

DATE _____

LAUNCHING SITE _____

_____

TIDE _____

WIND _____

OCEAN/MARINE/SURF/BUOY _____

_____

PADDLE INFO _____

PADDLE PARTNERS _____

_____

TRIP GOALS _____

_____

ESTIMATED MILEAGE _____

NOTES

DATE _____

LAUNCHING SITE _____

_____

TIDE _____

WIND _____

OCEAN/MARINE/SURF/BUOY _____

_____

PADDLE INFO _____

PADDLE PARTNERS _____

_____

TRIP GOALS _____

_____

ESTIMATED MILEAGE _____

NOTES

DATE _____

LAUNCHING SITE _____

TIDE _____

WIND _____

OCEAN/MARINE/SURF/BUOY _____

PADDLE INFO _____

PADDLE PARTNERS _____

TRIP GOALS _____

ESTIMATED MILEAGE _____

NOTES

DATE _____

LAUNCHING SITE _____

_____

TIDE _____

WIND _____

OCEAN/MARINE/SURF/BUOY _____

_____

PADDLE INFO _____

PADDLE PARTNERS _____

_____

TRIP GOALS _____

_____

ESTIMATED MILEAGE _____

NOTES

_____
_____
_____
_____
_____
_____
_____
_____
_____
_____
_____
_____
_____
_____
_____
_____
_____
_____
_____

_____
_____
_____

ATE _____

UNCHING SITE _____

_____

DE _____

IND _____

CEAN/MARINE/SURF/BUOY _____

_____

DDLE INFO _____

DDLE PARTNERS _____

_____

RIP GOALS _____

_____

STIMATED MILEAGE _____

NOTES

_____
_____
_____
_____
_____
_____
_____
_____
_____
_____
_____
_____
_____
_____
_____
_____
_____
_____
_____
_____
_____

DATE _____

LAUNCHING SITE _____

_____

TIDE _____

WIND _____

OCEAN/MARINE/SURF/BUOY _____

_____

PADDLE INFO _____

PADDLE PARTNERS _____

_____

TRIP GOALS _____

_____

ESTIMATED MILEAGE _____

NOTES

DATE _____

LAUNCHING SITE _____

TIDE _____

WIND _____

OCEAN/MARINE/SURF/BUOY _____

PADDLE INFO _____

PADDLE PARTNERS _____

TRIP GOALS _____

ESTIMATED MILEAGE _____

NOTES

DATE _____

LAUNCHING SITE _____

TIDE _____

WIND _____

OCEAN/MARINE/SURF/BUOY _____

PADDLE INFO _____

PADDLE PARTNERS _____

TRIP GOALS _____

ESTIMATED MILEAGE _____

NOTES

DATE _____

LAUNCHING SITE _____

TIDE _____

WIND _____

OCEAN/MARINE/SURF/BUOY _____

PADDLE INFO _____

PADDLE PARTNERS _____

TRIP GOALS _____

ESTIMATED MILEAGE _____

NOTES

_____
_____
_____
_____
_____
_____
_____
_____
_____
_____
_____
_____
_____
_____
_____
_____
_____
_____
_____

DATE _____

LAUNCHING SITE _____

_____

TIDE _____

WIND _____

OCEAN/MARINE/SURF/BUOY _____

_____

PADDLE INFO _____

PADDLE PARTNERS _____

_____

TRIP GOALS _____

_____

ESTIMATED MILEAGE _____

NOTES

Printed in Great Britain
by Amazon